Property of

Independent School District No. 833

Washington County, Minnesota

Grade_____4_____

No._13 N__ When Purchased _8/67_ Cost $ _2.64_

DATE	NAME OF BORROWER	CONDITION	
		Loaned	Ret'd
9/28/67	Eugene Farone		
	Joren Baily		
	JoAnn	1970	
		1971	
	michelle Pierce	1977	

The Harper & Row Basic Reading Program

Trade Winds

by Eldonna L. Evertts *and* Byron H. VanRoekel

HARPER & ROW, PUBLISHERS

Evanston, Illinois   Elmsford, New York   Pleasanton, California   New York, New York

Acknowledgments

Grateful acknowledgment is made to the following authors and publishers who granted permission to reprint these selections:

"Other People's Weather," an adaptation of pages 57–75 of *Big Steve, The Double-Quick Tunnelman* by Marie Bloch. Reprinted by permission of Coward-McCann, Inc. Copyright 1952 by Marie Halun Bloch.

"Counters" by Elizabeth Coatsworth. Reprinted by permission of Coward-McCann, Inc. from *Compass Rose* by Elizabeth Coatsworth. Copyright 1929 by Coward-McCann, Inc.

"Brands," an adaptation of pages 1–9, 13–21, 29–33, 51–56, and 63–68 of *The Cowboy's Own Brand Book* by Duncan Emrich. Copyright © 1954 by Duncan Emrich. Published by Thomas Y. Crowell Company, New York. Reprinted by permission of William Morris Agency, Inc.

"Little Leaguer's First Uniform," an adaptation of pages 74–99 from *Little Leaguer's First Uniform* by C. Paul Jackson. Copyright © 1952 by C. Paul Jackson. Thomas Y. Crowell Company, New York, publisher.

"If Only," from *Gay Go Up* by Rose Fyleman. Copyright 1929, 1930 by Doubleday & Company, Inc. Reprinted by permission of the publisher. Canadian permission granted by The Society of Authors as the literary representative of the Estate of the late Rose Fyleman.

"E" from *All Around the Town* by Phyllis McGinley. Copyright 1948 by Phyllis McGinley. Published by J. B. Lippincott.

"Snow in the City," by Rachel Field. Reprinted with permission of The Macmillan Company from *Branches Green* by Rachel Field. Copyright 1934 by The Macmillan Company, renewed 1962 by Arthur Pederson.

"Charlotte's Web," an abridgment, with an added introduction, of Chapters IX, X, and XI of *Charlotte's Web* by E. B. White, illustrated by Garth Williams. Copyright 1952 by E. B. White. Reprinted with permission of Harper & Row, Publishers, New York.

"The Story of Pa and the Bear in the Way," a reprinting of excerpt from pages 109–113 of *Little House in the Big Woods* by Laura Ingalls Wilder. Copyright, 1932, as to text, by Laura Ingalls Wilder; Copyright, 1953, as to pictures, by Garth Williams. Harper & Row, Publishers, New York.

The following adapted selections are reprinted with the approval of the authors and by permission of Harper & Row, Publishers, New York.

"The Biggest Nobody," an adaptation of pages 38–61 of *Depend on Katie John* by Mary Calhoun. Copyright © 1961 by Mary Calhoun. Adaptation approved by Mary Calhoun.

"The Talking Cat," an adaptation of pages 17–29 of *The Talking Cat* by Natalie Savage Carlson. Copyright, 1952, by Natalie Savage Carlson. Adaptation approved by Natalie Savage Carlson.

"The Buffalo Hunt," an adaptation of pages 123–138 of *The Tomahawk Family* by Natalie Savage Carlson. Copyright © 1960 by Natalie Savage Carlson. Adaptation approved by Natalie Savage Carlson.

Illustrated by:

Andy Aldrich	Bart Jerner	Rick Schreiter
George Armstrong	Herb Kane	Maurice Sendak
Ed Augustiny	Richard Kenyon	Amos Sewell
Bruce Bomberger	John Langston	Fritz Siebel
Jack Breslow	Don Madden	James Teason
Muriel and Jim Collins	H. Charles McBarron	Thornton Utz
James Curran	Tak Murakami	Aldren Watson
David Davies	George Porter	Garth Williams
John Downs	Harold Price	Paul Williams
John Henry	Bill Randall	Jan Wills

Contents

*Indicates that a **word highlight** will be found at the end of these selections.

4

5

Unit One

Adventures and Sports

Words You Can Pronounce

Each group of words has the same vowel sound.

bat	den	fist	shot	dump
grab	sped	chin	stock	stuff
pant	press	dim	prop	slug
scalp	chest	strip	bond	struck
scrap	melt	pitch	flock	pump

Use the vowel sounds you have reviewed and pronounce these words.

scramble	tangle	wiggle	chuckle
temple	ramble	fiddle	prickle
stumble	tremble	struggle	crackle
trample	kindle	muzzle	buckle

Sentences You Can Read

Tom, did you <u>unmuzzle</u> that fox?

Ted cannot <u>unbuckle</u> the strap on his cap.

Ben will <u>untangle</u> the string after lunch.

When can Sam <u>unscramble</u> the mess in that box?

<u>Unsaddle</u> the black horse when you get home.

8

Mrs. Treat   Toby   Mr. Lord   Ben   Mr. Treat

TOBY AND MR. STUBBS

In the late 1800's Toby Tyler ran away from his uncle's farm to join a traveling circus. By day he sold candy and by night he rode with Old Ben who drove the monkey wagon.

Toby soon found that circus life was not as pleasant as he had thought it would be and he determined to run away as soon as possible. Mr. and Mrs. Treat, the skeleton and the fat lady, were kind to him. But Mr. Job Lord, who ran the candy booth, treated him harshly.

One night, as the circus was on its way to a new town, Toby found a very special friend and became a hero.

Toby and Ben climbed up on the high seat of the monkey wagon. Minutes later Ben had his team moving slowly down the dusty road in a line with the other circus wagons.

"Well," said Ben, when he had his team well under way, "how did you get along today?"

Toby told Ben everything that had happened to him. He told about the candy man's unkindness and Mrs. Treat's present. Toby ended his story by saying, "That was one of Mrs. Treat's doughnuts that I just gave to Mr. Stubbs."

"You gave a doughnut to Mr. Who?"

"To Mr. Stubbs—the old fellow here in the cart, you know. He's been so good to me."

Ben chuckled and then asked, "How did you know his name was Stubbs?"

"Oh, I don't know that that's his real name," was Toby's answer. "I only call him Stubbs because he looks so much like a boy I knew at home who had that name. He doesn't seem to mind because I call him Stubbs."

Ben looked at Toby for a minute, acting all the time as if he wanted to laugh again. Then he said, as he patted him on the head, "Well, you are the funniest little fish that I ever saw in all my days.

You seem to think that the monkey knows all you say to him."

"I know he does," said Toby with determination. "He doesn't say anything right out to me, but he knows everything I tell him. Do you suppose he could talk if he tried to?"

"Look here, Toby"—and Ben turned half around in his seat and looked Toby in the eye—"are you crazy enough to think that the monkey could talk if he wanted to?"

"I'm not crazy," said Toby thoughtfully. "But I never saw any animal like this old Mr. Stubbs before. I think he could talk if he wanted to. One time Mr. Stubbs grinned at me. How could he do that if he didn't know what I'd been saying to him?"

"Look here, my boy," said Ben, in a fatherly way, "monkeys aren't like people. They don't know how to talk any more than they know what you say to them."

"Didn't you ever hear any of them say a word?"

"Never! I've been in a circus many, many years and I never saw anything in a monkey but monkeyshines."

"Well," said Toby, "I believe Mr. Stubbs knows what I say to him, anyway."

"Now don't be silly, Toby," said Ben. "You can't show me one thing that a monkey ever did because you told him to."

Just then Toby felt someone pulling at the back of his coat. When he looked around, he saw a little brown hand reaching through the bars of the air hole of the monkey cage.

"There!" he said to Ben. "Look there! I told Mr. Stubbs if he wanted anything more to eat, to tell me and I would give it to him. Now you can see for yourself that he's come for it." And Toby took a doughnut from his pocket and put it into the tiny fist. "Now do you think Mr. Stubbs knows what I say to him?"

"They stick their paws up through those bars all the time," said Ben. "Why, I've had them pull at my coat in the night until they made my skin prickle. You see, Toby my boy, monkeys are monkeys; and you mustn't get the idea that they're anything else. You think that old monkey knows what you say? He doesn't. He keeps his eyes on you. Then he tries to do just as you do, and that's all there is to it."

Toby would have believed all that Ben had said if, just at that second, he had not seen that brown fist reaching through the hole to grab his coat again. Toby put another doughnut in the tiny hand, and then sat thinking.

For a time they rode without talking. Ben was whistling without making a sound, and Toby's thoughts were far away in the home he had left.

Toby's thoughtfulness had made him sleepy. His eyes were almost closed, when he was startled by a loud noise. He had a feeling of being dumped from his seat, and then he lay senseless by the side of the road. The wagon was wrecked and all of the monkeys were escaping. Ben knew at once from the noise that his wagon was breaking down. Without having time to tell Toby of the trouble, Ben had

jumped off the wagon. It was the breaking of one
of the wheels which Toby had heard just before he
was dumped from his seat.

When the wagon came down upon the hard road,
the monkeys scrambled off in every direction. By
chance, when Mr. Stubbs started for the woods, he
came across Toby who was senseless on the ground.
The monkey stopped and carefully examined Toby.

He put a little brown hand into the boy's pockets and tried to look in his half-closed eyes. Luckily for Toby, he had fallen upon some mud and had fainted for only a minute. When Toby came back to his senses, the sad-faced monkey was busily examining Toby's ears, nose, and mouth. Toby knew that the sad look on the monkey's face showed that he was worried.

"Don't worry, Mr. Stubbs," said Toby, as he sat upright and looked about him. "I didn't get hurt; but I would like to know how I got over here."

It really seemed as if the monkey was pleased to know that his little friend was not hurt, for he smiled—or that was what the boy thought.

By this time the news of the wreck had been shouted ahead from one team to the other, and all hands were coming to the wrecked wagon to try to help. As Toby saw the men coming, he also saw some small animals scampering down the road. For the first time he understood why Mr. Stubbs was free, and knew that those little dark figures were the other monkeys escaping to the woods.

"See there, Mr. Stubbs! See there!" he exclaimed, pointing toward the runaways. "They're all going off into the woods! What can we do?"

The sight of the runaways seemed to excite the old monkey just as much as it did the boy. He jumped to his feet, chattering in the most excited way. Mr. Stubbs screamed two or three times, as if he were calling them back, and then started off after them.

"Now he's gone too!" said Toby, miserably, believing the old fellow had run away. "I didn't think Mr. Stubbs would treat me this way!"

The boy tried to get to his feet, but he felt so dizzy and sick from his fall that he sat down again. Meanwhile the crowd around the wagon paid no attention to him. He lay there without making a sound until he heard the cross voice of Mr. Lord asking if his boy were hurt.

The sound of Mr. Lord's voice made Toby shake with fear. His heart beat so loudly that he thought Mr. Lord must know where he was by the sound. But when the candy man did not come directly toward him, Toby had the idea that now would be a good chance to run away. He rolled himself over in the mud until he reached the grass along the road. Then he scrambled to his feet and sped toward the woods, following the direction the monkeys had taken.

Toby no longer felt dizzy and sick. His fear at the sound of Mr. Lord's voice had taken care of all that, and he felt well again.

He walked for some distance—far away from the sound of the voices in the road. Suddenly he was surprised to see a line of small figures coming directly toward him from the trees.

Toby could not understand the meaning of this strange crowd until he heard a chattering from the leader of the party. He recognized the chattering of the old monkey who had left him just minutes before. He knew now that the strange figures were the escaped monkeys. They had been overtaken by Mr. Stubbs, who was bringing them back.

The old fellow was leading the band, and all were walking "hand in hand" with each other. They came up to Toby, half hopping, half walking upright, and all chattering and screaming.

Toby stepped toward the noisy crowd. He held out his hand to the old monkey and said, "I felt so miserable because I thought you had gone off and left me. Now I know that you went to find the other fellows. You're very good, Mr. Stubbs; and now, instead of running away, as I was going to do, we'll all go back together."

The old monkey grabbed Toby's hand with his free paw, and held tightly to it. The entire crowd followed in unbroken line, chattering and scolding angrily. Every now and then Mr. Stubbs would look back and scream out something, which would make the monkeys stop their noise for a minute.

It was really a funny sight, but Toby seemed to think it was the most natural thing in the world that they should follow him in this way. He chattered to the old monkey quite as fast as any of the others were doing. He told him all that he knew about the wreck, and explained why he was running away. Toby really believed that Mr. Stubbs understood every word he was saying.

Very soon after Toby had started to run away, the owner of the circus came to the wreck. After seeing that the wagon was being fixed so that it could be pulled to the next town, he ordered that everyone should look for the monkeys. It was very important that they should be found at once. He seemed to worry more about the escape of the animals than about the wrecked wagon.

While the men were making plans to look for the runaways, the disturbing noise made by Toby and his party was heard. The men stood still to learn what it was.

The workmen shouted with laughter as Toby and his friends reached the wreck. The wagon was now standing upright, with the door open. Toby took the monkeys to it and directed them to get into the cage.

The old monkey stepped back to Toby's side. He screamed at the others in such a way that they all went into the cage, leaving him on the outside with the boy.

Toby directed Mr. Stubbs to get in, too, but he scolded so angrily that everyone knew that he had no idea of leaving Toby. One of the men stepped up and was about to push Mr. Stubbs into the cage, when the circus owner ordered him to stop.

"What boy is that?" he asked.

"Lord's new boy," said someone in the crowd.

The owner asked Toby how he had found all the runaways.

Toby answered, "Mr. Stubbs and I are good friends. When he saw the others running away, he just stopped them and made them come back to me. Please let Mr. Stubbs ride with me; we like each other."

"You can do just what you please with Mr. Stubbs, as you call him," said the circus owner with a smile. "I thought half of the monkeys in that cage would escape, and you have made every one come back. That old monkey is yours. You may put him in the cage whenever you want to, or take him with you, just as you like, for he belongs entirely to you."

Toby smiled happily and picked Mr. Stubbs up in his arms. The old monkey patted Toby's face and chattered softly. Even hard-hearted Mr. Lord saw how much the two loved each other.

That night Mr. Stubbs fell asleep in Toby's arms in the bandwagon. Toby chuckled to himself and whispered, "Tomorrow will be a good day."

Circus is a Latin word meaning "circle" and is related to the Greek word for "ring." When we talk about a three-ring **circus**, we are really repeating ourselves.

Easy Words to Pronounce

clam	bet	stick	clock	club
flap	spend	trim	flop	stump
faint	treat	wide	bar	sport
aim	fear	wipe	harm	cork
gain	scream	stride	chart	thorn
fame	beef	throat	roost	field
pale	free	boast	smooth	chief
stake	keen	coach	shoot	shriek

Compound Words in Sentences

We could hear a drumbeat from the bandstand.

The locksmith opened the box on the tugboat.

The brickyard is near that last boxcar.

For a year that shortstop has been my teammate.

The green campstool is in the back bedroom.

Out West a pancake is often called a flapjack.

He fixed the drainpipe on the drugstore.

Our landlord saw the missing plane in the cornfield.

Jack wanted his nickname on the classroom chart.

A broomstick is larger than a chopstick.

Hank
Speck
Umpire

Skinny
Red Kutter
Jerry

Fred
Johnny
Pudge

LITTLE LEAGUER'S FIRST UNIFORM

Johnny Cook is one of the youngest members of the Tigers, his Little League team. When his team wins the Regional Championship, he is overjoyed. Of course he has no hopes of playing in the Little League World Series because only the older boys will be chosen. Then his brother Hank catches the mumps. Johnny gets to go to Williamsport with the team and wear Hank's uniform! In the last game, Johnny isn't to be given a chance to play. But when Fred hurts his ankle, Johnny is asked to take his place.

On the day of the last big game the Tigers kept telling themselves that it was only another ball game. But each boy knew better!

"No use in a fellow trying to fool himself," Speck said to Johnny. "This isn't just another game. IT'S THE CHAMPIONSHIP GAME!"

Johnny felt queer and empty inside.

"We sure have bad luck," Skinny said loudly. "First Hank gets sick. Then Fred is hurt."

"Coach said that real champions overcome bad luck," Johnny said quietly.

"That's right," Skinny scowled. "But I'd feel better if Fred were in the line-up."

"Aw-w-w-w, Johnny will do all right," Pudge said. "He fielded the one chance he had Monday all right."

Skinny nodded, "Yes, he caught an easy fly. But did you see the throw he made to Speck?"

Johnny remembered Monday's wild throw and felt weak and sick. He pounded his fist into his glove. He HAD to snap out of it. He COULDN'T disgrace Hank's uniform!

During infield practice, Speck tossed a roller to Johnny. He fielded it and threw carefully. His throw was straight and true—right into Speck's glove. Johnny felt a little easier.

"That's the way to throw the old ball!" Speck cried. "You have the stuff, Johnny!"

It was nice to hear, but was there a little worry in Speck's voice? Snap out of it, Johnny told himself angrily. Speck and Pudge and Jerry are pulling for you. But Johnny knew that the rest of the team felt shaky about him.

Then the Coach started to bat grounders to the infielders. He batted a nice easy hopper to Johnny. Johnny fielded the ball and threw to Speck. It was a good throw. Speck threw to the catcher. Johnny took a toss from the catcher and threw swift and true to the third baseman. The ball sped around the infield.

"That's the old stuff in there! The way to go!" Pudge yelled from the outfield.

Johnny began to feel easier. Coach is right, he told himself. It's just like any other game.

Practice time ended. A voice gave the Tiger line-up over the loudspeaker. The batting order for the team from Florida was given.

The umpire-in-chief went to the home plate. The base umpires took their places behind first and third base. The umpire at home plate dusted off the base. He straightened and tossed a ball toward the mound.

"Play ball!" the umpire cried.

The Tigers ran on the field shouting to each other. They shouted encouragement to Jerry who would pitch today.

The first Florida batter waited out Jerry. The first two pitches were balls. Then there were two strikes. The boy from Florida swung on the fifth pitch. It was a sharp hit toward Johnny!

Johnny did not stop to think. There was no time to think. His short legs carried him across the grass. He pushed his glove out and the ball hit the pocket. Johnny's throw to Speck was a good one. It beat the runner by four steps.

"That's the way to grab that old ball, Johnny," Speck cried. "Told you that you had the stuff!"

Suddenly the emptiness was gone from Johnny. Things were going to be all right. The team was not weaker with him in the line-up. He was not going to disgrace Hank's uniform.

A shout came from the stands. "Hey! The peanut looks like a ballplayer!"

Johnny felt warm and good.

Johnny's turn at bat did not come until the third inning. He did not feel so empty inside now, but there was still a little shakiness. After the Florida pitcher finished his practice pitches, Johnny stepped into the batter's box.

"Cook, Number 19, now at bat," a voice announced. Then there came a chuckle over the loud-speakers. Johnny looked so different from the other batters. Hank's uniform hung loose and baggy on him. The cap was too big and the pants hung almost to the ground. Only an inch of Johnny's socks showed above his shoes.

"We had better explain ourselves," the voice said. "Up here beside us in the press box is Red Kutter, the well-known radio sports announcer. Red just said something over the air that we think fits very well. He said, 'Here comes the uniform, where is the boy? All-Pants Johnny Cook is now at the plate!' "

Howls of laughter came from the crowd in the stands. It seemed that everyone in the world was laughing at Johnny Cook.

Johnny pulled back deeper into his oversize uniform. He felt empty and shaky again. Things had been shouted at him before about his size, but this was somehow different. Suddenly he became really angry. He grabbed his bat tightly. He would show them.

The first pitch was a foot above Johnny's head. He swung wildly at the ball and missed. His swing was so hard that he fell and landed in the dust on the seat of his pants.

More howls of laughter! Tears filled Johnny's eyes. He was miserable. He wished he could dig a hole in the ground and sink into it.

The Florida catcher grinned down at Johnny. He tossed the ball to his pitcher. He made believe that he was afraid of Johnny's big swing.

"Keep it away from this slugger," the catcher yelled to the pitcher. The words were for Johnny's ears. "If he gets untangled from that uniform, he might slug one! If!"

Johnny struck out. He didn't even touch the ball with his bat.

The Tigers did not score. The game was half over and neither team had scored. Then Florida scored a run in their half of the fourth inning. They had a base on balls and two safe hits. Johnny was glad that they had not hit toward him. I would have done something wrong if they had, he told himself.

Johnny sat alone when his team came off the field. He looked up when a voice said his name.

"Johnny," the voice said, "believe me, I'm sorry." It was Red Kutter. "I should never have said anything like that. There is one big trouble with people who talk over a radio. They think they have to say something smart."

Johnny said nothing. He felt as though he would never be able to say anything again. His throat was full of an ache.

"You can't let the crazy thing I said get you down," Red Kutter went on. "Johnny, the big-league stars almost all have nicknames. Those nicknames are trademarks. The thing I hung on you is a trademark."

Babe Ruth "Sultan of Swat"

Carl Hubbell "Old Square Pants"

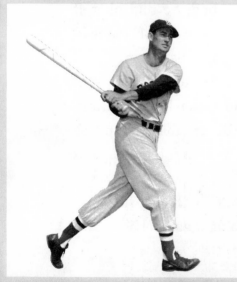

Ted Williams "Splendid Splinter"

Stan Musial "Stan the Man"

Still Johnny said nothing. The voice of Red Kutter changed. "You have to pull yourself out of the dumps, Johnny. You must do it for your team. You must!"

Then Red Kutter left, and Johnny went out to his place in the field at the beginning of the next inning.

The first ball was hit toward him. Johnny fielded it and threw it to Speck. He heard a sound behind him. Skinny had run over to back him up. Johnny knew that Skinny had expected him to miss the ball.

Something began to stir inside Johnny. What if a fellow *was* little? It did not take a giant to play baseball. He would show them. The next time at bat he would knock the ball over the fence, just as Hank would do if he were here. He would show them that size of a fellow's uniform did not count.

In the bottom of the fifth inning, the score was still 1–0 against the Tigers.

"We've got to get some runs," Pudge said. "Get on base, Pete. We'll knock you around."

"Get on," Johnny said, "and I'll knock you around!" He looked at his teammates. He looked at them hard.

"Somebody had better knock someone around," Skinny growled.

Pete got on base. Johnny came to the plate full of determination. He shut his ears to the laughter that came up from the stands. He swung with all his might at the first pitch. His hit was far from a home run, but it was a safe hit. The Tigers now had runners on first and second base.

Skinny came to bat. He hit the first pitch hard and squarely. It was a long hit. Pete and Johnny crossed the plate and Skinny reached third base.

The Tigers were ahead! The score was 2–1.

It was still 2–1 at the end of the inning. No other Tiger could get a hit to bring Skinny home.

"The old ball game is in our pockets!" Speck yelled. "We got the old championship!"

"We only have to get three fellows out," said Johnny who felt wonderful. He had helped the team! He was not disgracing Hank's uniform.

Jerry struck out the first two Florida boys to face him. Then Jerry got into trouble. The next three Florida batters reached base. A safe hit would score two of them, perhaps all three.

The next Florida boy swung hard on the first pitch. It looked as if the safe hit had come. The boys on the bases ran like the wind. If the ball dropped safely they would score.

Johnny took one look at the ball. His short legs pumped over the ground. He could never reach it.

But he had to! The long pants legs moved back and forth very fast.

Suddenly it seemed as though the oversize pants had tripped Johnny. But it was not a fall. Johnny saw that he was not going to reach the ball. He gave a wild leap and slid on the grass. His chin almost dug into the ground. His gloved hand stretched as far in front of his body as he could reach. The ball fell right into the pocket of the glove. It was a lovely, white thing against the brown of the glove. Johnny held it tightly. He scrambled to his feet and waved his glove at the umpire who had run toward him.

The umpire waved his arms and shouted, "Fairly caught! Batter's out! The game is over!"

The scoreboard still showed a beautiful big 2 for the Tigers and 1 for Florida. The Tigers were Little League World Champions!

Johnny was surrounded by his teammates. They yelled. They laughed. They pounded him on the back. They hammered each other. They cheered.

Then Johnny was lifted high on his teammates' shoulders. He grabbed a shoulder and looked down. The shoulder belonged to Skinny.

Skinny grinned up at Johnny and yelled something. Johnny couldn't hear but he grinned back and nodded. They loved each other. Everything in the past was forgotten.

"All-Pants Johnny Cook! Plenty of uniform and plenty of boy!" Red Kutter's voice came over the loudspeaker. "Hi, Johnny! We're all proud of— THE UNIFORM THAT WALKED LIKE A BOY! ALL-PANTS JOHNNY!"

Johnny's grin was wide and happy. Why, Mr. Kutter was right. He did not mind the words. He liked them. They were *his* trademark!

At one time an **umpire** was called a *numpire*, but the spelling of words can change. "Numpire" came from two Latin words, *non* and *par*, meaning "not equal or even." How does this meaning relate to our use of the word *umpire*?

THE STORY OF PA AND
THE BEAR IN THE WAY

"When I went to town yesterday with the furs I found it hard walking in the soft snow. It took me a long time to get to town, and other men with furs had come in earlier to do their trading. The storekeeper was busy, and I had to wait until he could look at my furs.

"Then we began to bargain about the price of each one, and then I had to pick out the things I wanted to take in trade.

"So it was nearly sundown before I could start home.

"I tried to hurry, but the walking was hard and I was tired, so I had not gone far before night came. And I was alone in the Big Woods without my gun.

"There were still six miles to walk, and I came along as fast as I could. The night grew darker and darker, and I wished for my gun, because I knew that some of the bears had come out of their winter dens. I had seen their tracks when I went to town in the morning.

"Bears are hungry and cross at this time of year; you know they have been sleeping in their dens all winter long with nothing to eat, and that makes them thin and angry when they wake up. I did not want to meet one.

"I hurried along as quick as I could in the dark. By and by the stars gave a little light. It was still black as pitch where the woods were thick, but in the open places I could see, dimly. I could see the snowy road ahead a little way, and I could see the dark woods standing all around me. I was glad when I came into an open place where the stars gave me this faint light.

"All the time I was watching, as well as I could, for bears. I was listening for the sounds they make when they go carelessly through the bushes.

"Then I came again into an open place, and there, right in the middle of my road, I saw a big black bear.

"He was standing up on his hind legs, looking at me. I could see his eyes shine. I could see his pig-snout. I could even see one of his claws, in the starlight.

"My scalp prickled, and my hair stood straight up. I stopped in my tracks, and stood still. The bear did not move. There he stood, looking at me.

"I knew it would do no good to try to go around him. He would follow me into the dark woods, where he could see better than I could. I did not want to fight a winter-starved bear in the dark. Oh, how I wished for my gun!

"I had to pass that bear, to get home. I thought that if I could scare him, he might get out of the road and let me go by. So I took a deep breath, and suddenly I shouted with all my might and ran at him, waving my arms.

"He didn't move.

"I did not run very far toward him, I tell you! I stopped and looked at him, and he stood looking at me. Then I shouted again. There he stood. I kept on shouting and waving my arms, but he did not budge.

"Well, it would do me no good to run away. There were other bears in the woods. I might meet one any time. I might as well deal with this one as with another. Besides, I was coming home to Ma and you girls. I would never get here, if I ran away from everything in the woods that scared me.

"So at last I looked around, and I got a good big club, a solid, heavy branch that had been broken from a tree by the weight of snow in the winter.

"I lifted it up in my hands, and I ran straight at that bear. I swung my club as hard as I could and brought it down, bang! on his head.

"And there he still stood, for he was nothing but a big, black, burned stump!"

TERRY SETS SAIL

"This will be the best summer yet," said Terry to Great-Uncle Silas on the first day of his island vacation. And when Great-Uncle showed him the boat which was to be his very own, the summer seemed more wonderful than ever.

Terry named his small pram "Bluebird," and began planning the adventures he would have with her.

Every day Terry sailed "Bluebird" around the harbor. He nosed the little boat in and around the wide-beamed fishing boats and the sailboats of the summer people.

"Hi, 'Bluebird,'" they called, reading the lettering he had painted so carefully on his boat. "Having fun?"

And Terry nodded and smiled back.

Terry sailed his boat from one side of the harbor to the other. When there was a smart breeze, with sail full, "Bluebird" flew over the water.

"Really going places," the man at the store called, as he wiped his red hands on his apron.

"Sure thing," answered Terry.

But all the time Terry kept thinking, "This isn't adventure. Not real adventure."

So Terry went farther and farther into the salt ponds. He sailed "Bluebird" until all the fishermen's houses and the nets hung out to dry were out of sight. He sailed past the old windmill on the point and waved to the woman and her five children who had turned it into a summer house.

But still Terry didn't find adventure.

"I can't find any," he complained to Great-Uncle Silas.

"Well—the summer's still young," comforted Great-Uncle. "Sometimes you find adventure where you least expect it."

"Do you?" asked Terry hopefully. "Oh, well, I guess I'll go for a sail now and find the gulls down by the sand bar past the old windmill. Mary gave me a whole bag of scraps."

Great-Uncle took his pipe from his mouth and started to say something. Then, seeming to think better of it, he stuck the pipe back in his mouth.

There was a nice breeze and "Bluebird" sailed quickly out of the harbor, into the salt ponds, and past the old windmill on the point. In the distance Terry could see the long sand bar where the gulls roosted.

"They'll be glad when they see what I've brought," he thought.

Closer and closer "Bluebird" sailed toward the sand bar. Terry could see the gulls quite plainly. They looked just like Great-Uncle's wooden gulls. Only there were hundreds upon hundreds of them all perched facing the wind, eyes staring toward the water.

Nearer and nearer Terry sailed, but still not a gull stirred or turned a beady eye in Terry's direction.

"Bluebird" was sailing so fast that Terry was afraid he'd pass the sand bar before he could throw the gulls the scraps. So just as he came near the sand bar he turned "Bluebird" right into the wind. The sail began to flap in the breeze. Terry reached for the bag of scraps.

And then from the sand bar one gull shrieked. Upon this signal all the gulls flew into the air. Like a swift-moving cloud they flew between Terry and the sun. The air was filled with angry cries. The gulls shot like arrows down from the sky around "Bluebird." Then up they flew again shrieking.

"Here," yelled Terry above the noise and threw them up some bread.

But the gulls were so angry they didn't see the bread. They shrieked. They scolded. They dive-bombed around "Bluebird." Their long bills looked sharp and mean when seen so close.

"Here, eat. Eat," screamed Terry fearfully and threw more scraps.

But the gulls only seemed to grow angrier. Closer and closer they flew around "Bluebird." Only the flapping of "Bluebird's" sail seemed to keep the gulls from attacking.

Suddenly Terry was very frightened. It was mean of the gulls not to know that he had come wanting to be friends. They wouldn't even look at the bread he kept tossing into the air. All they seemed to want was for him to go, go, go. A shrieking gull flew so close over the bow of the little boat that Terry dropped the whole bag of scraps overboard in his alarm.

Terry was so frightened he wanted to cry. But a swift look around told him that it wouldn't be of the least use. There wasn't another boat within sight. The woman and her five children at the wind-mill on the point must all be indoors. There wasn't anyone to know of his trouble. He was all alone in the salt pond with the gulls.

He had to do something. He had to do it fast!

Rising to his knees in the bottom of the small boat, Terry waved his arms wildly over his head and shouted, "Get away. Get away. Get away."

The gulls flying closest to "Bluebird" were frightened and soared higher into the air.

Terry knew that this was his chance to escape. He quickly trimmed "Bluebird's" sail and steered her past the gulls' sand bar. For a little while the gulls shrieked around him. And still Terry shouted, "Get away. Get away!"

And then Terry noticed first one gull and then two or three others taking their perches once more at the far end of the sand bar. Pretty soon they all came to perch as before, facing the wind, eyes staring toward the water.

Terry gave a big sigh! He and "Bluebird" were safe.

When he sailed home across the pond, Terry was careful not to come near the sand bar. He could see a number of gulls diving over the spot where he had dropped the scraps.

"They didn't deserve the food, though," Terry said when he told the story to Great-Uncle Silas.

"Deserve?" questioned Great-Uncle. "You have to learn to look at it their way, Terry. They didn't ask you to come and disturb them, now did they? You wanted them to be thankful to you for bringing them food. But they didn't know that was what you were doing. And besides, they didn't need it. They can fish very well for themselves. Did you know they

will even dig clams? They'll fly way up in the air with a clam and drop it on the rocks below. Sometimes they'll pick up and drop the same clam four or five times until it's cracked enough so they can get the meat out of it. Wonderful thing—gulls."

Terry felt a little hurt. Great-Uncle seemed to be siding with the gulls.

"But you know," continued Great-Uncle, "seems to me you've had your brave adventure."

"What do you mean?" asked Terry.

"Didn't you say you wanted an adventure where you could be brave? I think you handled yourself right well. I'm proud of you."

"But—but I was scared," said Terry.

Great-Uncle smiled. "Everybody who's brave is scared first."

Alarm comes from the Italian *all'arme* which meant "to arms!" Later it also came to mean the "fear" felt by the people when they heard that order. Today *alarm* may also mean the mild warning of an alarm clock.

Some Words Have Different Meanings

Did you see him <u>scramble</u> to his feet?
Please help me <u>scramble</u> the eggs.

I will wash my hands at the <u>sink</u>.
He wanted to <u>sink</u> into the ground.

Jack drove a truck that <u>dumps</u> the sand.
The unhappy boy felt down in the <u>dumps</u>.

Did you see him <u>field</u> the ball?
We walked across the green <u>field</u>.

The hen can <u>perch</u> on the fence.
We ate the fresh <u>perch</u> for lunch.

Fred, bring water from the <u>pump</u>.
See his legs <u>pump</u> over the ground.

He will <u>pitch</u> the last game today.
The room was as black as <u>pitch</u>.

The newsmen sat in the <u>press</u> box.
<u>Press</u> down on the lid of this box.

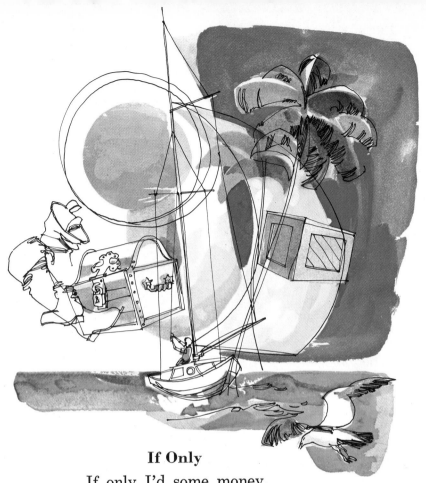

If Only

If only I'd some money,
I'd buy a jolly boat
And get a pair of sea boots
And a furry sort of coat,
A case or two of salted beef
And a seaman's wooden chest;
And I'd sail away to the North Pole,
Or I'd sail away to the South Pole,
Whichever I thought was best.

PIONEER FUN

Pioneers were people who settled in a new part of America. Their lives were different from the lives of many people today. Any neighbors they had usually lived many many miles away. Pioneer families did not get to see each other very often. Their life was quite lonely.

The pioneers also had to work very hard. Every day of their lives was filled with important jobs to be done. They had to raise their food, make their clothes, and build their own houses. Even the young children had to help. It took much determination to be a pioneer.

But pioneer life, though hard and lonely, was not all work. Pioneer families also had fun, but like everything else, they had to make their own fun. There were no football or basketball games. There were no teams to play these sports. There were no movies or TV. There were almost no books or newspapers to read.

So how did the pioneers have fun? Sometimes they got together. Just being together was an adventure.

Everything people did together, even work, was fun. It was an exciting treat to be with other families. So it was natural that the pioneers found some time to play when they got together to work. When a family had a big job to be done, neighbors would gather from great distances to help. They called this gathering a "bee."

The pioneers had many kinds of bees. In the spring they gathered to help each other plow the land and plant the fields. In the fall, when harvest time came, they helped each other again.

Sometimes the women and girls gathered for quilting or sewing bees. While they sewed they visited. They told each other what had happened to them all the days they had been alone. When they finished, they had quilts and clothes to keep their families warm—quilts and clothes which could not be bought in stores.

A house-raising was one of the best gatherings. When a family needed a house or barn, everyone from miles around came to help. The men and boys worked hard all day to lay the logs. Then they put on the roof, covered the windows, and made the door. Meanwhile the women cooked big meals for the hungry workers and the small children played.

At noon there was a lot of food but not much talk or nonsense, because they wanted to finish the house in one day.

Last of all, when the house was finished, a strip of deerskin was fastened to the inside of the door. The strip could be hung inside or outside. When pulled, it would raise the latch and open the door. Leaving the latchstring outside in the daytime was a sign of welcome. This is where the saying, "The latchstring is always out for you," comes from. It means "Come visit me. Open the door and walk in. You are welcome." At night, of course, the latchstring was pulled inside and the door was barred.

After the house was raised or the work was done, everyone was ready to have a good time. While they were eating supper, many tales and jokes were told. After supper they enjoyed contests, singing, and dancing.

The big boys and men often held contests. They never tired of seeing who could lift the heaviest weights, run the fastest, or shoot the best. These were things they needed to do each day and it was fun to prove who were the champions.

In most gatherings of pioneers there was a fiddle player who entertained them. Just listening to him was fun, but the people also liked to sing to his music. One of the songs they liked to sing was "Wait for the Wagon."

Besides singing, the people also liked to square dance to the music of the fiddler. Entire families joined in the dancing. From the time they were young, most pioneer children knew square dance figures such as "circle four" and "duck for the clam."

Late at night each tired but happy family would get in its wagon and start the long drive home. In the days of hard work and loneliness ahead, they would have many happy memories of the bee. They would eagerly look forward to the next time when they would get together for work and fun.

In France long ago, a foot soldier who went ahead of the main army was called a *peonier*. Our word **pioneer** means "a person who does something first." An early settler or anyone doing original work is known as a pioneer.

LITTLE SURESHOT

Each day Annie took her father's rifle down from its place on the cabin wall and went out into the forest. Life had never been easy for her family. Now that her father was dead, it was hard to get even enough to eat. With the rifle she could shoot wild game that lived in the woods.

Annie found that hitting the animals was easy for her. She almost never missed. Usually she brought home birds. What was needed for dinner they used. The rest she cleaned and packed in layers of grass in a basket. Later she sold them in the nearby town.

In those days most inns served wild game. The innkeeper in the town bought most of her birds and the rest were shipped to Cincinnati. People liked to buy her birds for they were always shot neatly through the head.

Now that Annie was earning money for the family, she was really enjoying life. She was being paid for doing the thing she liked best.

As the days went on, Annie enjoyed trying to make the shots harder. When a bird flew up, she would turn around in a circle before shooting it. Sometimes she would run a few steps and jump before hitting the bird on the wing. Each day she became a better shot.

At this time in America, the ability to use a rifle well was very important. With it, people could protect themselves from danger and get food to eat. It was only natural then that they should like to test their ability with a gun. The shooting match became a common sport. Usually it was only men who took part. Soon, however, the people who ate at the inn heard about the girl who had shot the game they enjoyed. She was asked to join them in their contests and she often beat even the best men.

One fall day when she took her basket of birds to the inn, the innkeeper said, "Annie, there's a man in Cincinnati right now who is very proud of the way he handles a gun. He is traveling with a show in which he does tricks with a rifle. He says that he can beat anyone who will shoot against him. I think you could beat him."

"Oh, I couldn't!" Annie exclaimed. "I'd be afraid to try."

"Why? You have shot against men around here," said the innkeeper trying to encourage her.

"Oh, that's different. I know them."

"Now, Annie," he continued, "I've already told this Mr. Butler that you would do it. It's important to me to keep my word. Please help me do that."

Annie thought the matter over and then said, "I'll try my best to win."

In a few days Annie arrived in Cincinnati where she was met by a married sister. Together they went up to the park where the contest would be held. From the top of the hill they could see the city below and the beautiful river winding through the hills.

"See that part of the city over there?" Her sister pointed out the spot to Annie. "We almost moved there. It's called Oakley."

"Oakley—" Annie repeated. "I like that name."

Before she could stop wondering about this strange and exciting city, she was met by the innkeeper. He led her to the shooting range.

"Annie," he said, "I want you to meet Frank Butler." He nodded to a big, blue-eyed man dressed in brown. The marksman wore a coat with large pockets and a soft green hat with a red feather in it. As she walked toward him Annie thought to herself, *he's the finest looking man I've ever seen. I wish I didn't have to beat him!*

Frank Butler stared at her in astonishment. "This girl? I thought I was to shoot against a man!"

"I said there was a crack shot from the backwoods," replied the innkeeper. "Here she is, Miss Annie Moses."

"But she looks like a child!" Mr. Butler exclaimed.

"She's young," agreed the innkeeper, "but she can outshoot you."

Then the marksman's face broke into a smile. He took off his feathered hat and bowed. "I'm surprised, but delighted, Miss Moses," he said.

"S-same here," was all Annie could manage.

Together they went to the shooting station and Annie was told to choose a gun. She picked one up and examined it. "I like the feel of this one," she said.

Mr. Butler explained that the man who ran the trap would pull a spring. Then a clay disk called a "pigeon" would fly up into the air. It would go in whatever direction the man wanted it to. He would try to fool the shooters. They could not raise the gun until they called, "Pull!"

Frank and Annie tossed a coin to see who would shoot first. Mr. Butler won the toss and took his place.

"Pull!" he called.

Up into the air flew the clay disk.

"Bang!" went Frank's gun.

"Dead!" called the referee as the pigeon was broken.

Annie stepped up. Suddenly she felt lost. Here was a strange place, a strange man, and a strange crowd watching her. Her knees began to shake and her arms felt weak. Then she thought of the woods at home and what it was like to shoot real birds. *You just swing with them*, she reminded herself. *You don't aim at them. When it feels right you shoot.* She would not miss.

"Pull!" she cried. With determination she raised the gun.

"Dead!" called the referee.

Each of them had twenty-five shots. It seemed as if the match would end in a tie. Pull! . . . Dead! Pull! . . . Dead! Pull! . . . Dead! So it went. Finally it was time for the last shot.

"Pull!" called Frank Butler. His gun spoke a little too late.

"Miss!" came the shout.

"Pull!" called Annie in a calm voice.

"Dead!" cried the referee.

Annie had won the match!

Frank Butler turned and smiled as he shook her hand. "Miss Moses, I should feel badly to be beaten by you, but you are a wonder with a rifle. May I take you and your sister to see my show tonight?"

Annie didn't know what to say.

"We'd like to," her sister answered for her.

That show was one Annie would always remember. She had thought that shooting was just shooting. Now she learned that tricks could be done with a gun that would be interesting and exciting for people to watch.

She saw a helper hold up a playing card, which Butler shot through the middle. Then, from the bottom of a glass turned upside down, he shot off a cork. Finally an apple was put on the head of a small dog. Butler neatly shot the apple in two. Then

the dog grabbed the pieces in his mouth and ate them. *I could do those tricks*, thought Annie. And a new world of fun and adventure was opened to her.

Annie went home thinking that it had been a most wonderful day. Little did she realize that her life had been changed. Little did she know that in one year she would be Frank Butler's wife. In two years she would be his partner in his act and would take the stage name of *Annie Oakley*. In six years she would be the star, and he her manager. In eleven years she would be one of the best-known women in America. Crowds would recognize and follow "Little Sureshot" wherever she appeared.

All her life she would never forget that it all began one fine day in Cincinnati, with the cry of *Pull!* ... *Dead!* ringing through the clear November air.

 Sometimes a free ticket to a show or a game is called an **Annie Oakley**. When the free pass has a hole punched in it, the ticket looks like one of the cards Annie pierced through the center during her shooting act.

Sound and Spelling

dew	coin	they	loud	perch
chew	joint	hey	mound	berg
crew	boil	grey	snout	nerve
head	boy	clay	drown	draw
breath	joy	pray	scowl	crawl
spread	toy	gray	crowd	spawn

Sounds of "ed"

chewed	jointed	perched
coined	headed	shrieked
crawled	crowded	wiped
prayed	melted	corked
scowled	rounded	stumped
smoothed	boasted	clocked

"Run away from that wall!" shouted the fireman.

He coached his men for the big game.

The stream forked on the other side of the hill.

The water from the fire plug sprinkled the crowd.

We boiled the water before we drank it.

Fern threaded the needle easily and quickly.

ANDROCLES AND THE LION

In the days of the Roman Empire, about two thousand years ago, whenever a man seriously broke the law he was made to fight a fierce lion barehanded. The Romans had built great open-air arenas where people could come to watch this uneven contest. These arenas were much like our present-day baseball or football stadiums. Quite often the men who were made to fight the lions were captured runaway slaves, for in those days it was a great crime for a slave to try to flee his master.

One afternoon a man named Titus was working in his little shop near the arena. Suddenly he heard a mob coming down the street shouting and cheering excitedly.

"To the arena! To the arena!" The screaming crowd pushed through the streets. Titus ran from his shop and was caught up in the crowd. Another runaway slave had been captured and everyone was on the way to see him fight a lion.

People surrounded Titus on all sides. So many people were crowding into the narrow street that he thought he would not be able to move.

When Titus finally reached the arena, there were hundreds of people pushing their way up the huge stone steps. He scrambled through the shouting crowd and dropped onto a seat. As soon as he had caught his breath he was on his feet again shouting, "Bring him on! On with the sport!"

On the far side of the arena, a door opened. A man was tossed into the ring and fell in the sand. The heavy door closed and the crowd fell silent as the man pushed himself slowly to his feet.

A fierce roar came from the other end of the arena. Everyone turned to see an iron gate being swung aside. A huge lion who had been caged, beaten, and starved for several days sped from behind the bars and into the ring.

The crowd shrieked with delight as the maddened beast rushed the helpless man. The slave took one

step backward, lost his footing, and fell to the ground. He lay there trembling with his face hidden in his arms. In a second he would be dead.

A man behind Titus shouted, "On your feet!" Everyone was shouting. People had come to see a fight, not this!

The lion got ready to attack. Suddenly, before the surprised crowd, he walked up to the slave and began to lick his hands and face. The crowd grew silent as the slave threw his arms around the lion and petted his big head.

"Explain!" came a lone cry from behind Titus. The crowd took up the cry and soon the air was filled with the shout, "Explain! Explain! Explain!"

The slave moved calmly to the middle of the ring with the lion following at his heels like a pet dog. With one hand the slave patted the lion's head and with the other he made a sign for the crowd to be silent.

When everyone was quiet, the slave began speaking in a loud, clear voice. "My name is Androcles. I have broken the law. Months ago I ran away from my master. His cruel treatment was more than I could bear. For many days I hid in the woods far from the city.

"One evening I was sitting, cold and lonely, under a large tree. Suddenly I was startled by the roars

of an angry lion. The roaring grew louder as he came nearer. I knew that he would surely attack me. Before I could hide, he was upon me. Then, in the half darkness, I saw that he was walking on three legs. He was holding one of his front paws off the ground as if it ached. As he came closer to me, his roaring became less fierce and I became less fearful.

"I gathered my courage and touched his paw. The lion seemed to realize that I was his friend and stopped his roaring. As I grew braver, I ran my fingers over the paw. There, deep in the poor animal's foot, was a prickly thorn! I took the end of the thorn in my hand and gave it a quick pull. Out it came! The lion licked his paw, then he licked my hands. Truly, I think he was trying to thank me for what I'd done!

"From that day to the day I was captured, this lion and I were friends. And that is our story."

Androcles looked up into the silent crowd. They had come to see a fight. Were they disappointed? Would they call for another lion?

Androcles' throat grew dry and his heart pounded wildly. Each second seemed like a lifetime.

Finally a voice shouted, "Freedom!"

"Freedom! Freedom!" other voices began crying.

"Freedom for Androcles and the lion!" The entire arena was filled with the excited cries of the people who had come to see Androcles die.

That evening Titus told his family about the strange thing that had happened at the arena that day. Because of the friendship between Androcles and the lion, they had been set free. For once, the law had not been carried out.

Arena is a Latin word which means "sand." In early Rome the ground where men fought against wild beasts was covered with *arena*. Today we call the space where a contest is held an **arena**.

Unit Two

World of Nature

Sounds of "c" and "g"

class	code	greet	gain
classes	codes	greets	gains
classed	coded	greeted	gained
classing	coding	greeting	gaining
price	lace	rage	judge
prices	laces	rages	judges
priced	laced	raged	judged
pricing	lacing	raging	judging

Silent Letters

doubt	wreck	budge	half	calf	comb
climb	pledge	ghost	limb	wren	folk

I need two slices of bread and one of meat.

Do you know who wrote the pledge to the flag?

The fringe on that scarf is tangled.

The diver plunged into the water near the wreck.

He asked, "What is the price of that sledge?"

Have you ever seen a wren eat crumbs?

They are judging the songs of the folk singers.

The raging storm broke many huge tree limbs.

The ghost was greeted with laughter by the crowd.

POLLIWOG

Until early last summer Joseph Pond's nickname had been Joey. But then his family moved to a new town. When Joey met the boys in the neighborhood, one of them said jokingly, "I know a better nickname for you—Polliwog." *Polliwog,* because Joey was the smallest of everybody, just like the wriggly little polliwogs which were the smallest frogs in the pond across the street.

The nickname stuck and Polliwog made many new friends that summer. When school started, he was enrolled in Miss Weaver's class.

It was a warm day for fall. Polliwog sat in Miss Weaver's class and looked out the window and prayed for rain. It had looked like rain when he started out for school, and he had brought his raincoat. Now the sky kept getting brighter. Polliwog sighed a big, sad sigh.

He wanted it to rain because there was a hole in his pants. It had happened when he reached over to pick up his pencil. Suddenly he'd heard this terrible ripping sound—ri-i-i-p!

So far he was all right. He hadn't had to stand up for anything. What he was worrying about was when everybody marched out at recess. Polliwog was a room captain. He stood at the landing, halfway down the stairs between the second floor and the first.

It wouldn't be so bad while he was standing there. He could keep his back to the wall. Going outside afterward—that was the real problem. That was why he wanted it to rain. If he wore his raincoat, it wouldn't matter about the hole in his pants.

Usually Polliwog was lucky, but today the sun came out more and more. He had made up his mind, though, and shortly before the bell for recess Polliwog stood up. He turned and walked carefully to the coatroom, taking short steps. He came out with the raincoat on.

The whole class looked at him, then looked out the window at the sun. Miss Weaver did, too. She murmured something, but Polliwog hurried from the room, raincoat flapping around his knees.

He stood at the landing, and the marching out began. Polliwog's older brother Frankie came by with his class. All the way down, Frankie stared at him and his raincoat. He had to look back over his shoulder by the time he got to the bottom of the steps. Polliwog's class came by. Polliwog turned his eyes from all the faces that asked, Why?

Now it was suddenly quiet. Usually Polliwog raced down the stairs after the last marcher. Today he hesitated. If he went out for recess, everybody would look at him and ask why he was wearing his raincoat. If he took it off, they'd laugh at him.

Polliwog stayed on the landing. He looked out the window. Maybe if he delayed long enough he wouldn't have to go outside at all. He noticed the lock on the window. It was a kind he had never seen before. This window had the lock at the bottom and it was in the middle of the window, not at the side.

Polliwog curiously opened and closed the lock. It looked as though you couldn't lock a window like this when it was raised. He turned the lock, noticing how it worked.

A footstep sounded. A sharp voice startled him. "What are you doing there?"

It was the janitor. It sounded as if he were blaming Polliwog for something and Polliwog didn't know how to answer. He could answer that he was standing here, but the janitor could see that. He might think he was being smart. What did he want him to say?

"I'm—I'm—" Polliwog began.

"You were fooling with that lock!" the janitor said.

Polliwog looked at his hands. He had opened the lock and closed it, all right. He had looked at the lock. "What do you mean?" he asked.

The janitor grabbed Polliwog's shoulder. "Come with me."

Polliwog was hustled down the steps and outside. Then they went around the corner of the building and into a section that Polliwog had never entered before. There he saw huge pipes and heard strange sounds. He saw the biggest fan he had ever seen. Everything was iron.

The janitor sat down on the only chair. "What's your name?"

"Pol—Joseph."

"Joseph what?"

"Pond."

The janitor shook his finger at Polliwog. "I want your real name. Don't try to fool me. Pond! Pond! I can get it upstairs, so you might as well tell the truth."

Pond didn't sound much like a real name. Polliwog tried to think of one that would sound better, but the janitor was so mad that Polliwog couldn't think straight. He thought of Mark. Mark's last name was Hunter. Hunter? The janitor wouldn't believe that either. He thought of Tom Peters. "My last name is Peters," he said quickly.

"Now, that's more like it. Tell the truth and we'll get along better."

"Yes, sir."

"Why were you fooling with the lock?"

"I was just looking at it."

"Why weren't you outside like everybody else?"

Polliwog just shook his head.

"Why weren't you?" It was louder this time.

"I didn't want to be. And that's all I'll tell."

The janitor looked at him. It was a hard look. "I'm taking you to the principal's office."

They went up a different set of stairs this time. The janitor led Polliwog into the office—past a lady, a clock, and a place for mail, keys, and reports. Finally they went through a door.

The principal, who wore glasses, sat behind a big desk. The janitor spoke rapidly. "I caught this boy on the landing by the south stairs. He was unlocking the window. His name is Joseph Peters."

The principal looked calmly at the janitor, and with friendly curiosity at Polliwog. He said, "Thank you. I'll call you if I need you."

The janitor hesitated, then left. Polliwog bet he would like to have stayed.

The principal said, "Let's see—Peters? Hmm! I didn't know Tom had a brother."

Polliwog hesitated. He didn't know what to say.

The principal said, "Do you happen to know John and Frankie Pond? and Joseph?"

Polliwog said, "Those are my brothers." He was all mixed up. "I mean John and Frankie are my brothers. Joseph isn't my brother, because *I'm* it. I mean 'Joseph' is MY name."

The principal said, "Did the janitor get mixed up?"

"He didn't believe it when I told him my name. He thought the name 'Pond' was a joke. I couldn't think of any other name but Peters. But it wasn't Peters, it was me."

"It was you who did what, Polliwog?"

Polliwog was startled. The principal had called him *Polliwog!* "Do you know everybody at school?" he asked.

"Just about." The principal's eyes went to the raincoat. "Aren't you too warm with that coat on? Why don't you take it off?"

"I can't. I tore the seat of my pants."

It had come out before Polliwog thought. It was too late now. It was bad enough for anybody to know, but now the principal of the whole school knew.

The principal wasn't laughing at him, though. He was just smiling a little. "Keep the coat on if you'd rather. Mrs. Block has some thread and other sewing things, though. If you like, you can wait here while she fixes the rip."

Polliwog's eyes opened wide. "You mean in your office?"

The principal nodded. "I have to be away a few minutes. You can hand your pants out the door to Mrs. Block. Don't let anybody in until I get back."

Polliwog almost jumped out of his skin. Was he dreaming? "Don't let anybody in"—that's what he'd said. It sounded as though Polliwog was the head of the whole school. He kept the raincoat on and handed the ripped pants out the door.

In a few minutes the job was done. Polliwog took off the raincoat and sat by the principal's desk and waited. Soon the principal returned.

"Feel better, Polliwog?"

"You bet."

"You stayed by the window because of the rip in your pants?"

"Yes, sir."

"I'll tell you something, Joseph. Don't tell anybody, though. This is a secret. I had a rip, too, when I was about your age. It was terrible."

"Yes, sir."

"I'm going to tell you why the janitor was worried. Someone broke into the school a few nights ago."

Polliwog felt suddenly angry. He had looked at that lock. But it didn't mean he was going to break into the building. He was angry that the janitor didn't trust him. He didn't say anything, though.

"The janitor has a big job," the principal said. "He can't very well know all the boys and girls. I just told him we can trust any of the Pond boys."

"Thank you."

"You may go now. And, Joseph . . . "

"Yes?"

"If you ever need any sewing done, let us know."

In England about five hundred years ago a **polliwog** was called a *polwygle.* They used *poll* which means "head," and *wygle* which means . . . can you guess? Do you think "wigglehead" is a good name for a young toad or frog?

THE LAKE THAT FLEW

Hank Huggins sat atop a rail fence, enjoying the fine spring weather.

"Hi, Hank!" a passing neighbor greeted him. "Pretty day, isn't it? Guess we'll have a spell of fine weather now."

"I wouldn't lay any bets on that," said Hank, looking doubtfully over toward the mountains. "You never can tell what the weather's going to do in those hills. Do you remember what happened to me that time I went out shooting geese on Dishpan Lake?"

"Can't say as I do."

"Queerest thing you ever heard of," Hank said. "It was in the fall of the year when it happened, when the wild geese were a-flying over on their way south. About twilight one night I noticed a big flock settle down on the lake. It was too dark then to get a good shot at them, but I made up my mind to get up early and be on hand at sunrise to pick off a few when they took off. A nice roast goose would taste mighty fancy, I thought.

"Well, sir, I was up early, just as I'd planned to be. It was nice weather for fall, not too hot and not too cold, and it didn't show any sign of changing. But let me tell you it did change, and that in a hurry. The wind changed and blew clouds over the mountains. Before I knew what was happening, it was way down below freezing. I could feel the grass cracking under my feet. The bushes snapped like glass breaking. The dew on them had turned to ice. Everything was frozen solid. I was pretty cold myself and hustled along as fast as I could, to keep my blood warm.

"I got to the lake about sunrise. What I saw there really surprised me. There were geese all right, a big flock of them, but such a noise I never heard in my life. They were mighty upset about something; I could tell that. The way they were acting wasn't natural. One would flap his wings as hard as he could, as if he wanted to take to the air, but he never moved from that pond. Then another would try it, and another and another.

"I stood there on the bank for a spell, wondering what in all get-out was the matter. Then it came over me what must have happened. The lake had frozen over suddenly while those geese were asleep. It had caught their legs tight in the ice, and now the geese were stuck like flies on flypaper.

" 'Jumping frogs!' I said to myself. 'What a piece of luck. These geese can't get away. I can walk right out there on the ice and knock off enough to last me a year. I won't even have to use my gun.'

"I tried the ice to see if it would hold my weight. It was frozen as hard as a rock, so I walked out toward a big gander. I started to knock him on the head with my gun. But it wasn't going to be as easy as I thought. That fellow had a mighty long wingspread. He fought at me, hitting me in the face, knocking off my hat, and batting the gun clean out of my hands. I saw I'd have to shoot him, so I backed off a little, took aim, and fired.

"Well, sir, the report of that gun roared over the lake like a thunderclap. It frightened those geese half out of their lives, and every pair of wings beat the air at once. At the same moment, from all around the edges of the lake, there came a loud cracking sound. Then I felt the ice moving under my feet. I didn't know what to make of it. It was going up—up—up into the air. Before I could realize what was happening, I found myself above the treetops. Those geese, all working together, had lifted that frozen lake right out of its bed! They were flying away with it and with me, too, for I was standing right in the middle of it.

"I never was in such a fix in my life. When I looked down, my blood almost froze. There below was the church. My house was nearby, looking no bigger than a matchbox and getting smaller every minute.

" 'Jumping frogs! How am I going to get down from here?' I said to myself. It was too late to jump, that was certain. I told myself I'd better make the best of it and stay right there until the geese decided to make a landing. They'd have to settle down at nightfall for sure. But then it came to me that we were heading south, toward warmer weather. It wouldn't be long before that ice began to melt—and then what? I began to figure what I could do to get out of that fix.

"If I upped with my gun and killed off the geese with two or three shots, the lake would fall. I'd be cracked to pieces and so would the ice. Then I had a bright idea. It was what finally solved the problem and saved my life. I took aim with my gun and shot one gander. The lake dropped just a bit nearer the ground. By now the big ganders were so winded they gave up, one by one. We dropped down as softly as landing on a feather bed. It was just in time, too, for the sun had got mighty hot.

"I waited around until the last of that lake melted away, and then I gathered up the geese. There was a pile of them as high as a barn, and I had to hire a wagon to carry them all home.

"My wife was a bit surprised to see what a load I had. She said, 'For the land's sake, Hank! You sure were lucky to bring these geese down.'

" 'Annie,' I said to her, 'I was still luckier to bring myself down.' "

The syllable *twi-* means "two or double." So **twilight** means that time which is between the day and the night. Tell how the idea of two is reflected in the meaning of <u>twin</u>, <u>twenty</u>, <u>twelve</u>, <u>twice</u>, and <u>twist</u>.

Vowels in Accented Syllables

motel (mō tel′)   solid (sol′id)

rejoin (rē join′)   polish (pol′ish)

omit (ō mit′)   punish (pun′ish)

Schwa in Unaccented Syllables

spider (spī′dər)   problem (prob′ləm)

moment (mō′mənt)   gander (gan′dər)

human (hū′mən)   distant (dis′tənt)

frozen (frō′zən)   dragon (drag′ən)

pupil (pū′pəl)   western (wes′tərn)

minus (mī′nəs)   signal (sig′nəl)

major (mā′jər)   pistol (pis′təl)

siren (sī′rən)   medal (med′əl)

The major signaled for the pistols to be fired.

The pupils will rejoin the class at any moment.

It is a big problem to see those small spiders.

The distant motel is on the western side of town.

He will be minus a dragon if he omits that page.

When the gander landed, the ice was frozen solid.

Only a strong human being can win that medal.

The sound of the distant siren awakened us early.

ALASKA

Muir Glacier

JOHN MUIR

In the summer of 1880, John Muir left for his second trip to Alaska. On his first trip the year before, he had discovered a new glacier which had been named for him—Muir Glacier. Now he wanted to study the surrounding countryside more carefully. As the boat landed in Alaska he saw his old friend, Mr. Young, who had come down to pick up the mail.

"When can you be ready?" Muir shouted to his surprised friend. "Get your boat and men and let us be off."

Soon they were ready for the trip—a trip Muir would always remember because of a little dog named Stickeen.

The boat had been made ready and the Indians they had hired as guides were there. Soon Mr. Young appeared, followed by a little black dog. When Young stepped aboard, the little dog jumped in and curled up on a coat.

"But such a helpless animal will only be in the way," Muir complained. "This trip will not be easy for a small dog."

"Stickeen won't be any trouble," Young answered. "He's a wonder dog. He can stand cold and hunger like a bear. He swims like a fish and is very wise and clever." He stopped because he couldn't think of any more nice things to say. Stickeen just lay there wagging his tail.

The dog went along.

Muir studied him as the small boat moved through the water. He was no particular kind of dog—just an odd mixture. He had a long, wavy, black coat and a very fine tail that curled almost to his nose. His keen dark eyes took in everything that happened.

When the men spoke of stopping, Stickeen would sit up, look over the shoreline carefully, dive overboard, and be the first to land. Then, moving softly like a fox, off he would go to hunt for small game. When the men were ready to leave they could never find him. Finally, when the boat was out in the water, the dog would jump in and swim after it. Sometimes he had to swim a long way, but he seemed to love it.

When they camped, the Indian guides would go into the woods to hunt for deer. Muir would wander off to study the countryside. On every trip the dog trotted after him. He seemed to like Muir's company.

At last the group came to the edge of a large glacier. Muir decided to start early the next morning to explore it. He was so excited about it that he got up before the rest of the men were awake. He even forgot to eat breakfast, but he did take along some bread. Before he had gone far, Stickeen came running after him.

"No you don't, little fellow," said Muir. "It will be no trip for a dog in a storm like this." But a very wet Stickeen just stood there dripping. He did not budge. "It would be as hard for the earth to lose the moon," growled Muir. "Oh well," he grinned, "if you're so determined, come along." He gave the dog some scraps of his bread which Stickeen chewed quickly. Then they started off together.

In the morning hours they climbed up the east side of the mountain through forests of fallen trees. They reached the ice river itself. Muir made ax steps up the glacier, which Stickeen easily followed. As they went, Muir took compass readings. This was so they could find their way back if the rain changed to snow. At last they stood on the top of the glacier. The ice stretched as far as the eye could see.

Now they crossed to the west side. On the way they saw big crevasses, or cracks, in the ice. Some of them were more than twenty feet wide and nearly a quarter of a mile deep. Luckily, they were able to go around the larger ones. The smaller ones they jumped. Muir was surprised at how easily the little dog leaped cracks that were six to eight feet wide.

After reaching the west side, they turned north. Here the walking was easier for they were along the edge of a forest. Muir saw that many of the trees and rocks had been mashed by the ice.

Suddenly they came upon an icefall, like a frozen waterfall, two miles long. They followed it and Muir saw that it ended in a lake that was full of icebergs. He wanted to explore the lake but he saw that the afternoon was almost gone. Soon it would be dark and he must be home before nightfall.

As they started the return trip, snow began to fall. Soon it covered everything. Muir knew the direction of the camp, but could not follow the exact path he had taken. He thought about spending the night on the glacier, but was afraid that he and the dog would freeze to death. So cold, wet, and hungry, they continued on their way.

They came to a crevasse. Gathering their nerve, Muir and Stickeen jumped across. But now facing them was a huge crack nearly fifty feet wide. After walking up and down along it, Muir discovered that it was fastened at both ends to the one they had just crossed. They were on an island of ice and there was no escape!

This was a matter of life and death, but Muir was not one to give up easily. Carefully he looked over the edge of the big crack. Far below he saw a narrow bridge of ice leading to the other side. Could he cross it? Perhaps by cutting holes in the ice with his ax he could make steps down to the bridge. But would Stickeen be able to follow? He would have to try. There was nothing else to do. Through the blinding snow Muir leaned down and began cutting a hole.

Just then Stickeen pushed his head past Muir's shoulder. He looked down, and then up quickly. There was a startled look on his face. He whined as if to say, "You can't take us into that terrible place!"

"Don't be afraid, little fellow," Muir spoke to him, trying to calm his own fears. "We will get safely across, but it won't be easy. We must take a chance if we are to save our lives."

But Stickeen would not be calmed. With a sharp bark he ran off to try to find another crossing. When he came back, Muir was already in the center of the bridge of ice. He sat on it with his legs hanging down on either side to steady himself. Slowly he edged forward, always looking straight ahead.

The hardest part came when he reached the other side. He must stand up and cut steps in the ice wall in front of him. How he got up he never knew. Somehow he found himself on the other side.

When Stickeen saw that his master was safe, he whined louder than ever. He looked down and then ran back and forth as if to say, "I can't *do* it. I *can't* follow you!"

Muir shouted to him crossly. "You *have* to do it. I can't wait any longer. If you don't try it now, I'll have to leave you here."

The dog understood. Very slowly he slid his feet over the edge. From step to step he inched downward until he stood on the narrow bridge. Then, steadying himself against the wind, he crawled forward. When he reached the end he paused, as if studying the steps. Then suddenly, in a springing rush, he leaped up and whizzed like a rocket right past Muir's head. It was all so fast Muir could not see how it was done.

"Well done, my friend, well done!" Muir shouted. But Stickeen didn't hear a word. He was running and rolling; scampering and screaming. It was as if he were crying, "Saved! Saved! Saved!" For a few minutes Muir was afraid such exertions would kill Stickeen.

There was still some distance to go before they reached camp. Muir started running. Over and over again Stickeen shot ahead like an arrow. At last the mountains could be seen and soon they reached solid rock.

At ten o'clock that night, when Mr. Young and the guides had about given up hope of their return, Muir and Stickeen stumbled into camp. Too tired to eat, Stickeen lay down on his blanket in the tent. The men helped Muir change his wet clothes and gave him some food. Not until he had finished eating did he speak. Then looking toward the corner he said, "There's a brave doggie!" Stickeen opened one eye and weakly pounded his tail.

During the rest of the trip Stickeen never left Muir's side. At night around the campfire the dog would put his head on Muir's knees and look up at him as if to say, "Didn't we have a terrible time together on that glacier?"

After Muir left Alaska he never saw Stickeen again. But throughout Muir's life, as he sat around the evening campfires, he often told the story of their exciting adventure on the glacier.

Flea

My dog presented me today
With just one little flea.
He missed it not at all, but, oh—
The difference to me!

Footprints

I love a field of smooth clean snow
Untouched by any human feet
And when I have to walk through one
I try to make my footprints neat.

Monkeys

I stood before the monkey's cage,
Their funny ways to see—
I laughed at them a lot until
I saw one laugh at me.

Respelling for Pronunciation

poison (poi′zən)

section (sek′shən)

canyon (kan′yən)

powder (pou′dər)

center (sen′tər)

sentence (sen′təns)

package (pak′ij)

stallion (stal′yən)

mixture (miks′chər)

glisten (glis′ən)

Three-Syllable Words

poisonous (poi′zən əs)

sectional (sek′shən əl)

collection (kə lek′shən)

alphabet (al′fə bet)

difficult (dif′ə kult)

numeral (nü′mər əl)

Primary and Secondary Accent

cemetery (sem′ə ter′i)

gunpowder (gun′pou′dər)

indistinct (in′dis tingkt′)

reservation (rez′ər vā′shən)

Our zoo has a large collection of poisonous snakes.
The Indian reservation is near the small canyon.
The glistening mixture was in a large package.
Each letter of the alphabet is in that sentence.

WILD STALLION OF THE PLAINS

Many are the tales that have been told about a mysterious wild white stallion. He is said to have appeared now and then on the plains of the American West.

Some who saw him thought that he was not a real horse at all but just a drift of mist. They called him the Ghost Horse of the Prairies.

Others were sure he was real. But whatever he was, it seemed he did not grow old. Indians and cowboys caught glimpses of him for over a hundred years. Yet no one was ever able to catch him. Although many tried, they found the stallion was faster and stronger than any other horse.

Only one person ever claimed to have touched the wild white horse. She was a young pioneer girl named Gretchen.

The Western plains stretched forever into the distance. The sun burned fiercely and the dust blew in endless circles. Still the wooden wheels of the covered wagon bumped along—on and on, on and on. In the wagon Gretchen rocked tiredly as the team of horses moved slowly through the prairie. Day after day went by with nothing to do, through miles and miles of the same uninteresting countryside. It was more than a girl could stand.

Gretchen rested her chin on her hands. She folded her arms behind her back. She raised her arms above her head, then swung them down hard —back and forth, back and forth. She brought them to rest in her lap and leaned forward.

"Ma! Pa!" she called. "Please, may I ride the pack mare for a while?"

Her father turned his head, keeping a loose hold on the reins. "But, Gretchen, that mare is carrying our sacks of corn meal."

"I know, Pa, but I'm not so very heavy, and it would be something different."

"Oh, Joseph," her mother said, "do you think she should? I'm afraid she might fall off."

"Nonsense, Betty, we'll tie her legs to the sacks. Besides, the mare is a gentle one. Gretchen won't be hurt."

Her father stopped the team and waved to Gretchen to climb out of the wagon. He lifted her to the mare's back and tied her tightly to the pack. Then they started up again, the mare keeping pace with the wagon team.

Gretchen found riding the mare much more interesting than sitting in the wagon. She could at least feel the breeze, though it wasn't a cool one.

After an hour or so the sky darkened. Gretchen looked up. Ahead of her, clouds covered the sun. *It must be raining over there*, she thought. But as they moved into the area, the rain stopped. Still the air was warm and sticky, and the ground, soft and muddy.

Suddenly she realized that she was not riding beside the wagon any more. Quickly she looked back over her shoulder and saw what had happened. The wagon wheels were sunk deep in the mud. Turning her attention back to the mare, she brought her to a stop.

For a time she watched as her father hunted for stones and branches to put under the wheels. They should keep the wheels from slipping. But the work took quite a long while. The sun came out again. It was so warm and the ride had been so tiring! Gretchen felt her eyes growing heavy and soon she was fast asleep.

She awakened with a start. A loud whinny had disturbed her dreams. Or was she still dreaming? She was by a riverbank. The old mare must have been hungry and wandered over for a meal. But the mare wasn't eating now. Her attention, like Gretchen's, was directed to the other side of the riverbank. Across the water was the most beautiful stallion Gretchen had ever seen. He was all white and his long mane seemed to shine like strands of silver in the sun. He whinnied again and stamped his feet. It was as if he were saying, "Follow me. I am your leader."

The old mare gave an answering whinny and the next thing Gretchen knew they were swimming through the river. When they reached the other side, the stallion turned and galloped off in the direction of the distant hills. The mare followed, trying to keep up with the fast pace set by the stallion. They flew across the prairie as if on wings. The ride so excited Gretchen that she forgot to be frightened.

The stallion led them on—through a narrow canyon and into a beautiful green valley. Ahead of them, a herd of horses turned as one to watch as the newcomers came nearer. Then in a rush the wild horses galloped to meet them. They gathered around the old mare and began sniffing the sacks of corn meal curiously. Then they started nipping to get at the meal. Some of the nips cut Gretchen's legs and, frightened now, she began to cry.

Suddenly the white stallion was beside her, pushing and driving the others away. Then he turned his attention to the ropes that tied Gretchen to the pack. With a few quick bites he snapped the ropes. Then his strong teeth tightened around her long dress. Carefully he lifted her up and gently set her down beside a little spring. After that he

reached for the meal sacks. He loosened these and set them down beside the girl. Then he stood waiting.

Slowly the other wild horses returned. They stood in a half circle facing Gretchen, with the old mare and white stallion in the middle. It was as if they were expecting something of her.

Gretchen looked from one to the other and then began to open the sacks of corn meal. She poured some out and placed it before the stallion. Now some for the old mare. Then for each horse in turn she poured out a little pile of meal. Still they waited. At last she helped herself, and all together they began the feast.

This is fun, thought Gretchen. *It's like a party. I'm the hostess for the white stallion's corn meal party!*

Gretchen cupped her hands to take up some water from the spring. She began to drink eagerly. By the time the horses had also taken a drink, the stars were beginning to shine. Then the herd moved slowly away. Only the mare and the stallion stayed near her. Gretchen closed her eyes.

When the first rays of sun began to shine on the valley, she awakened. She stood up to stretch. Yes, there were the two horses nearby. She walked over to them and gave them each a pat. She spoke softly to them. "Thank you for watching me through the night."

Now Gretchen started to climb up on the old mare, but try as she might, she could not do it. She felt a gentle tug on her dress. In a second the white stallion had lifted her and placed her on the mare's wide back. He whinnied once, and then before Gretchen could give him a parting pat, he was off like the wind. She watched until he disappeared behind the hills. Then holding the old mare's mane tightly, she began the long journey back through the canyon and across the prairie. Another swim across the river brought her safely to the covered wagon, where her worried parents greeted her gladly.

She never saw the wild white horse again, but as she grew older she often heard the cowboys tell of him. Many had tried to rope or trap the stallion, but only one cowboy claimed to have come near him.

Out on the open range the cowboy had built two stalls. He had lined them with the sweetest grains he could find. In one stall he had placed a beautiful brown mare. Then he had returned to his cabin to wait.

As he had hoped, the white stallion soon appeared, drawn by the grain and the lovely mare. But though a gate fell behind the stallion, the horse would not be trapped. The angry stallion turned the stalls into a pile of broken boards. The old cowboy watched in astonishment as the two horses galloped off together.

When Gretchen was a grandmother, she heard the cowboys tell of a new breed of horses they were taking in their roundups. They were stronger and swifter than any that had been captured before. And in color, they were silvery white spotted with brown. The cowboys called this new breed *pintos*, which means "painted ponies."

Of course no one could be certain, but both Gretchen and the old cowboy smiled wisely at the news. They were sure that the pintos must be the children of the beautiful brown mare and the wild white stallion of the Western plains.

The Latin word *canna* used to mean "reed" and was the first ancestor of our word **canyon**. It gradually changed in meaning, however, from *reed* to: a large reed, a large tube, a hollow; and, finally, to a deep valley with high sides—a canyon.

NATURE NEWS

Midnight Sun

During the summer the sun shines throughout the night in parts of Alaska. Even in the winter when the sun never shines, it is not completely dark. The snow-covered ground glistens from the light given off by the stars, the moon, and the northern lights.

Starfish

The starfish is a sea animal and not really a fish.

Most starfish have five arms, but some have as many as twenty-four. If one of these arms is lost, it will grow back. Or if a starfish is cut into several pieces, each piece will grow into a complete starfish if left in the ocean.

Asparagus

Asparagus is used both for food and decoration. The fern asparagus is often used for decoration, either alone or with cut flowers.

Raccoons

It's been said that raccoons will not eat unless they can wash their food first. It may well be true that a raccoon would rather wash his food if he could, but it has been proven that he is not likely to pass up a meal just because there is no water around!

Geese

Geese can fly higher than any other bird. They've been seen flying over the world's highest mountains—29,000 feet.

Spiders

Some spider webs are as much as six feet across. They are woven so strongly that some have trapped birds. In some countries people use these delicate but strong webs as fish nets. They have held catches of four pounds.

Grand Canyon

The Grand Canyon is the world's best-known canyon. It has been in the making for thousands and thousands of years.

A river has been slowly cutting through the rocks. At the same time the land in the area has been slowly rising. Weather forces have helped to make the canyon wider.

In overall size it is the largest canyon in the world.

Hills and Mountains

Land rising less than 2,000 feet above its surroundings is called a hill and land rising more than that is called a mountain. The longest and highest mountain range in the world lies under one of the oceans. In places the mountaintops break through the water and form islands.

Fleas

The flea can be made to do tricks. Flea circuses have troupes of trained fleas that do such things as pull tiny wagons.

Fleas are champion jumpers for their size. They have been known to jump 13 inches. This is about the same as a six-foot man jumping about 200 yards.

Buffalo

At one time great herds of
buffalo wandered the American
plains. Indians and pioneers
hunted them, and by 1889
only 551 were left. Game laws
were passed to protect them.
Today around 10,000 of these
animals live on game preserves.

A buffalo is a kind of wild
ox. Like the ox, its stomach
has four parts. Goats, sheep,
cows, and deer also have three
more parts to their stomachs
than people do.

Bears

The Brown Bear of Alaska
is the largest of all bears. He's
often 10 feet tall and 1,600
pounds in weight. Don't let his
size fool you—this animal can
run 30 miles an hour!

Horses

Before the white man came, American Indians had not seen horses. The Spanish first brought the animals to the Americas in 1519. Some of these horses, and some left by later explorers, most likely formed the beginnings of the wild herds of the West.

Veiltail Goldfish

Today pet goldfish are found in many parts of the world. However, their home is China. They were taken from there by traders who went to China hundreds of years ago.

Many goldfish are so colorful that they look as if they had been painted. The veiltail, with its wide, delicate tail, is a favorite pet.

Potatoes

The familiar white potato
was first grown in South
America. Today more potatoes
are grown in other countries
than in the Americas.

The white potato belongs to
the same family as the tobacco
plant—the nightshade family.

Icebergs

Icebergs may appear to be
different colors. Some look
white, some green, and some
even appear to be black.
Vegetable matter frozen in the
ice makes them look this way.

Weather

Weather records gathered
from around the world show
that at any given moment
there are about 1,800
thunderstorms raging!

THE CEMETERY GHOST

Homer Brown was late. He should have been home an hour ago, but it had been such a warm spring day that the boys had played ball until it was almost dark. He would have to hurry in order to get home in time to do his farm chores before going to bed. Hurriedly he walked down Main Street, the only street in town.

The Brown farm lay on the outskirts of the town. Usually Homer walked along the highway, but that was really the long way around. The road skirted a deeply wooded area that lay between the town and Homer's farm. Tonight the boy decided he would take the short cut. He quickened his pace as he neared the dark trees.

He rushed into the woods, but soon he found the going slower. There was only a narrow path to follow. It was lighted now by just a few rays of pale moonlight that found their way through the leaves. The path led through a cemetery in the middle of the woods. Carefully he picked his way around rocks, and pushed aside low-hanging branches. As he neared the cemetery, he turned up his collar and tried to walk a little faster.

Many scary stories had been told by the boys at school about this area. Homer really didn't believe them, but he couldn't help looking over his shoulder now and then just the same.

Soon he reached the first of the tombstones. It was newly decorated with flowers and looked quite harmless. Still he hurried on, past one and then another.

Something rattled. Homer stopped in his tracks. Wide-eyed he looked through the moonlit darkness. At first he saw nothing—just the ordinary sights of a quiet cemetery. Then something moved! Homer stared in growing alarm.

By the farthest tombstone, in the very direction in which he was going, an indistinct white shape appeared to bob up and down. For a moment Homer stood frozen, unable to move. He was held by the ghostly spell of the white shape that continued its bobbing.

When the thing came no closer, some of Homer's courage returned. Still he had no wish to find out what the thing was. Trying to make no sound, he crept slowly past the other tombstones. When the woods began again, he pushed ahead, unmindful of the cracking branches and rolling stones.

Once free of the woods he raced across the pasture, eyes straight ahead. He reached the house, slammed the kitchen door, and sank into a chair by the stove. Though the night was not cold, the warm stove seemed to comfort him. He placed his shaking hands along its side.

"Homer! For goodness sake, why are you so late?" His mother came into the kitchen at the sound of the slamming door. "Why, you look as white as a ghost!"

At the word *ghost*, Homer began shaking all over. "G-ghost," he muttered. "G-ghost in the cemetery."

His mother warmed a bowl of soup. "Here, this should help." She placed the bowl on the table.

Homer turned his chair around and began to eat. The hot soup seemed to calm him and soon he began to tell of his adventure. He spoke vaguely at first, and then warming to his story he started to add a few colorful happenings to make it sound more exciting. In the middle of his tale, Homer's father walked in and stood listening, an unbelieving look on his face.

"Seems to me I've heard such stories before, Son," he said. "Every time you've played ball with those boys and come home late, you've had some new ghost story to tell."

Homer hung his head. It was true. He had repeated the stories the boys told. Then he looked up, determination in his face. "But this time it's true, Dad—at least most of it. You must believe me. There IS something in that cemetery!" And Homer repeated the whole terrible adventure.

But it did no good. His mother and father had every reason to doubt his tale. They simply warned him to come home early next time—by the highway. Though it was late, Homer was sent to finish a few chores anyway, before going to bed.

Several days later, Mr. Brown drove into the town to check on a new tractor he had ordered. As soon as he walked into the store, the owner came up to him.

"Say, Mr. Brown," he questioned in a low voice, "have you heard about the strange happenings in the woods?"

"Strange happenings?" Mr. Brown looked curiously at the store owner. "Maybe yes . . . maybe no. What do you mean?"

"Well," the man went on, "the other night I cut through the woods. I was going to pick some flowers for my wife. It was her birthday, you know, and I'd forgotten all about it. I passed the cemetery. Everything seemed as quiet as it should be. Then —from over by the farthest tombstone—came a loud rattle! Something white was bobbing up and down. Believe me, I didn't stay long enough to investigate! Lucky thing I'd picked those flowers first. Strange. Most strange."

Mr. Brown agreed. *Yes, it was strange indeed,* he thought. And he told the man Homer's tale.

In the next few days many such tales were whispered about the town. Finally one night, Mr. Brown and a group of men decided to investigate the frightening stories. Armed with shotguns and small lamps, they made their way through the woods to the cemetery.

Nothing happened. Though they waited several hours, not a sound bestirred the silent night. At last, tired of their watch, they made their way through the cool spring air, back to their homes.

Still the ghost stories continued to be reported. So for the next two nights the men kept up their watch. Then late the third evening, around midnight, they were startled by a low moan. It sounded something like the lowing of a cow. The moan was followed by a dry rattle and soon their staring eyes made out a white shape. It began to bob up and down in the dark bushes by the farthest tombstone.

The almost-but-not-quite-frozen men uncovered their lamps. They made ready to shoot if the need arose. Quietly they crept closer. The shape continued bobbing and moaning. Mr. Brown decided to raise his gun. He fired into the air hoping to scare the ghost away. The shape stopped bobbing. But before the ghost could disappear, the men were upon it.

Shrieks of laughter resounded through the woods. Soon the men were holding their sides and rocking back and forth.

"Say, Brown," one of them howled, "you'd have done better if you'd brought a milk pail!"

For the mysterious "ghost" was nothing more than a white-faced black cow that had learned a new trick. Near the tombstone was a large bush. The cow had found that she could thrust her head through its branches. Then, by bobbing her white head up and down, she could scratch both sides of her neck at the same time.

Mr. Brown and the other ghost hunters crept silently away, grinning to themselves.

Tomorrow, Mr. Brown promised himself, *I'll fix that hole in the pasture fence.*

The other men most likely had quite different thoughts—of milking stools, perhaps?

A search for fingerprints may be made when a crime is investigated. If it is snowy or muddy, one might hunt for footprints. **Investigate** comes from two Latin words meaning "to follow a footprint."

Word Building

doubt	ghost	nature
doubtful	ghostly	natural
doubtfully	ghostlier	naturally
doubtfulness	ghostliest	naturalness
curious	safe	pain
curiously	safely	painful
curiosity	safety	painfully

The "ghost" wore a costume made of old sheets.
Ghostly sounds came from the center of the room.
Ben, your voice is ghostlier than Homer's.
Those low moans are the ghostliest sounds of all.

Frank was very curious about the unusual beetle.
He looked curiously at it and then called for Tom.
Their curiosity made them ask questions in class.

The scout troop went on a hike to study nature.
It is natural for this tree to lose its leaves.
Those leaves have changed their color naturally.
The naturalness of his last painting pleased me.
His first painting had unnaturally red leaves.

THE BUFFALO HUNT

Frankie Tomahawk lived on an Indian reservation in South Dakota. There, too, he went to school to learn the ways of modern Americans.

One day Frankie visited an Indian who believed in the old ways. The Indian thought it was silly to go to school. He told Frankie that one day the buffalo would return and sweep all other people into the sea. Then the land would belong to the Indians once more. At the end of the visit he gave Frankie a pet raccoon which the boy named "Little Brave."

Little Brave got into mischief at home, so Frankie decided to keep him at school. When the pet caused trouble there, Frankie was told to turn him loose.

Frankie Tomahawk was going to run away. He was going to live like an old-time Indian and never have anything to do with school or white people again.

Frankie held a small animal tightly in his arms. He wouldn't give up his pet. If he couldn't keep Little Brave at home or at school, he would live by himself out in the open. There he could keep Little Brave and have other wild animals as pets.

With determination Frankie turned his feet away from the school, slid under a wire fence, and stepped into the pathless prairie. From now on his life would be without paths to follow.

Frankie put Little Brave on the ground and began walking. The little animal trotted happily at his heels. The hills were ahead of Frankie. The wind was in his face. It made him feel free.

Now the ground became uneven. He walked with his head down to watch his footing.

When he raised his head to look about him, he saw the buffalo. Frankie stopped in his tracks. The great buffalo was coming out of the hills. And behind it, as far as Frankie's eyes could see, were moving bodies. The buffalo herd was coming back!

Frankie was filled with joy. At the time when he needed them most, the buffalo were coming back to drive the white people away and restore the prairie to the Indians.

Then a terrible thought flashed through his mind. What if the buffalo herd rushed straight for the school building? They could flatten it. The school belonged to him. It belonged to every Indian child. It would be terrible if their beautiful yellow desks were broken. The children would be hurt, and Miss Hansen, too.

His teacher had been kind to him many times but he hadn't even realized it until now. Miss Hansen had left her own family to come to teach Indian children. She had even understood how he felt about having to give up his pet.

Frankie actually felt sick. He must get back to the school before the buffalo got there. He must warn the teachers and children. Perhaps they could bar all the doors and withstand the buffalo attack.

He ran so fast that the muscles in his legs felt as if they were shot full of arrows. He ran like the whitetail deer. When he reached the schoolyard he paused for a moment to look back. The huge creatures were coming across the prairie.

Frankie rushed into his classroom with wild eyes. "The buffalo herd!" he panted. "It's come back! It's going to knock the school over!"

No one believed that he had seen the buffalo. They wouldn't do anything about it. Frankie's heart sank. There should be no delay.

He tried again when his breath was back in his body. "I really did see a buffalo, Miss Hansen," he repeated. "Dozens and dozens—a whole herd of them. And they're coming this way!"

But Miss Hansen could not believe it was true. She took Frankie and his problem to the principal.

"So you say that you saw dozens of buffalo on the prairie, Frank," the principal said doubtfully. "That is nonsense. You know that there are no longer any wild buffalo in this country. There are only the herds in parks and on ranches. There haven't been any wild herds around here for many years—since before your time."

"They've come back," said Frankie.

Then the principal looked out of the window. "You're right!" she cried. "There is a buffalo on the playground!"

They could see the buffalo. It looked like a great bull with a ragged brown carpet thrown over its head and shoulders. The huge creature was standing by the slide, sniffing over the playground as if it were thinking of using it for a pasture.

Then they saw a frightening sight. Frankie's little sister, Alice Tomahawk, was coming toward the playground from the road. She was walking with her head down. She would pass right near the buffalo.

Frankie didn't take time to wonder why his sister was on the playground. His bow and arrows were in the Indian collection Miss Hansen had started. He hurried to the table and grabbed his bow and two arrows. He rushed to the door and ran out.

The buffalo had seen Alice. It was going toward her now with its head down. Alice looked up when she heard Frankie coming. She saw the great beast and stopped dead in her tracks.

Frankie's arrow was pulled tightly against the bowstring. He ran close to the buffalo to get a better shot. Nothing ever looked bigger to the boy than that buffalo. Its huge back rose up like a mountain. Its woolly head was three or four times as large as a bull's. Its strong horns turned upward, and its tail was swinging slowly back and forth.

Frankie tried to keep his hand from trembling as he pulled the arrow back. It sped through the air and struck the beast on the shoulder, then fell to the ground. What a blunder! The buffalo looked at its small attacker with surprise, but it did not seem angry.

Frankie let the other arrow fly. It didn't even hit its mark, but the great beast stared at Frankie with a bewildered look in its little bloodshot eyes. Then it slowly turned and moved away. It must have thought that the old-time Indian hunters were coming back.

Alice had already gained safety in the classroom. Frankie felt foolish because he hadn't killed the buffalo. He hadn't even hit it the second time. But he was glad that his unexpected attack had scared the beast away.

Before he went back to the school, he collected his arrows. He looked up and down the prairie to see if the rest of the herd was coming. But there was no moving thing in sight other than the lone buffalo slowly walking down the road, swinging its tail and shaking its head. As the old bull walked, he kicked up little clouds of dust.

As Frankie went into the school, the principal was reporting to the children. "They told me at the reservation office that it is an old buffalo that was thrown out of the herd because it lost its fights with the young bulls," she said. "It has wandered all this way from the Black Hills. One of the Indians on the reservation had already called them because he saw it in the hills with his herd of cattle. They're sending a truck to take it back."

So *those* were the moving forms Frankie had seen among the hills—herds of cattle. There had been only one buffalo.

The children were curious about what would happen to the old buffalo when it was brought back to the herd. Would the young bulls turn on it again?

"No, indeed, they wouldn't dare," the principal smiled. "Not after it tells them its adventures on the reservation and how it was attacked by an Indian and lived to tell the story."

Miss Hansen turned to Frankie. "You were in the right, Frank," she said. "You really did see a buffalo."

"I wasn't *all* right. I intended to run away from school," he explained manfully.

Miss Hansen was surprised at this news. "But you came back," she said.

"I didn't want the buffalo to knock the school down," replied Frankie. "I thought there was a whole herd of them." He grinned sheepishly because he had thought the cattle were buffalo.

"Why didn't you want the school to be knocked down?" Miss Hansen followed up.

Frankie stood first on one foot, then on the other. His face got redder and redder. He wished his teacher would stop asking him questions. Finally he said, "Just because it's our school."

Suddenly Frankie remembered why he had run away! Little Brave! He had left his pet out on the prairie. He hoped with all his heart that Little Brave would find his way back to the Tomahawk cabin.

Miss Hansen's kind voice broke into Frankie's thoughts. "And do you still want to run away?"

Frankie swallowed hard. "I guess I'll stay here." He managed a weak grin. Then under his breath he added, "Maybe living on the prairie wasn't such a good idea after all."

The word **muscle** goes back to the Latin word *muscalus* which meant "a little mouse." Perhaps the Romans thought that the rippling of a muscle in an arm or leg looked like little mice playing.

Unit Three

Symbols, Signs, and Language

THE DAY FOR ENGLISH

For more than five weeks Candita had been
coming to school in New York but she had not yet
spoken English. When her teacher, Miss Singer,
spoke in English, Candita just smiled. She would
answer Miss Singer only when she spoke Spanish.
She understood, though, that the story the other
children were reading was about a squirrel.

"Rafael," said Miss Singer, "what is the squirrel's
name?"

"Bushy," said Rafael, standing up.

"His whole name," said Miss Singer. "What is the squirrel's whole name? Your whole name is Rafael Muñoz, isn't it?"

"That is my name," said Rafael. "And the squirrel's name is Bushy."

Alvaro raised his hand.

"Tell us, Alvaro," said Miss Singer.

"Bushy Tail," said Alvaro.

"That is right," said Miss Singer. "Very good, Alvaro." She turned to Candita and said slowly, "You see, Candita, Alvaro came only a few weeks before you to this class. Already he understands what we are saying. Alvaro learns quickly."

Candita looked at Alvaro. It seemed to her he had not understood either.

"Alvaro," said Miss Singer, "tell us how you came to New York."

Alvaro stood up and smiled but did not answer. He shook his head and lightly shrugged his shoulders.

"Alvaro, did you come from San Juan?"

"San Juan," repeated Alvaro.

"How did you come?" said Miss Singer.

"I come here," said Alvaro.

"How?" said Miss Singer. "Did you walk?" Miss Singer walked two fingers of one hand across her desk.

"Yes," said Alvaro, wishing to be agreeable. He smiled at the walking fingers. All the children laughed. Alvaro laughed, too.

"On the water? You walked across the water from San Juan to New York?" asked Miss Singer.

Candita held her breath and listened to each word. Why were they laughing? She, too, would say "Yes" to every one of Miss Singer's questions. The children would laugh at her just as they were laughing at Alvaro. Alvaro was brave. *If they laughed at me*, Candita thought, *I wouldn't laugh. I would cry. Yes, I would surely cry.*

Miss Singer began all over again. "Alvaro, did you come from San Juan to New York?"

"Yes," said Alvaro, still smiling.

"Did you come on a plane to New York?"

"Ah, yes," said Alvaro, understanding at last. "Plane."

"You came on a plane. You did not walk on the water."

"Ah, no," said Alvaro.

The children could not stop laughing.

Miss Singer held up her hand for silence and said to Alvaro, "Was it a big plane?"

"Big," said Alvaro.

"Yes," said Miss Singer kindly. "You came in a big plane. Sit down, Alvaro."

Alvaro dropped into his seat and drew a deep breath while Miss Singer wrote in a book.

In the little silence, Candita made up her mind: she would not say a single word. She would listen and say nothing. Even when she understood Miss Singer's question and knew the answer, too, she would not speak English. Only when she could talk like Miss Singer would she talk in school, not a day before. Only if Miss Singer talked to her in Spanish would she answer her.

She would not talk like a small child. She would not say *big, plane, yes, no.* She would speak

English when she could talk about the shining ocean the plane from Puerto Rico flew over, the beautiful clouds, and the plane itself.

She would wait. She would wait until she could talk well enough so they would all say, "Candita speaks well. She understands and speaks English very well. Was Candita born in New York?" She would wait until someone could say, "It seems to me Candita speaks as if she were born in New York."

At lunch, when the children were allowed to speak Spanish, Linda said to her, "You are too shy. You do not have to be shy, Candita. Miss Singer understands that everyone makes mistakes. I made many in the beginning. I do not make so many now, but I still make a few."

How could Candita tell Linda she wanted to say each English word right? She wanted to speak better even than Linda, who said she still made mistakes. No matter what Miss Singer thought, Candita would have to wait until she was sure all the words she said were right.

Linda said, "Look, Candita. We are both eleven. Alvaro and Rafael are older than we are. They will soon go to other classes. If you will try, we, too, can soon leave Miss Singer. This class is only for those who must learn to speak English before going to their true class, where they belong according to their age."

Leave Miss Singer? Candita did not want to leave her. When she did leave she would speak better English than any of her friends. She decided to learn the story of Bushy Tail word for word.

Weeks later she watched Rafael write *Tuesday* and *squirrel* and *house* and *train* and *plane* on the blackboard.

"Very good," said Miss Singer. "Erase the words, please. Erase." Miss Singer made the motion of erasing. "This is your last week here, Rafael," said Miss Singer. "Next week you are going up to Miss Wood's class. Will anyone else go to the blackboard?"

Candita knew all the words Rafael had written and many more besides. One day, she would surprise Miss Singer, but until then . . . Candita looked down at her desk.

The bell rang for lunch.

Today Candita did not feel hungry. She sat listening to the others begin to talk loudly in Spanish and heard the rattling of the papers as lunches were unwrapped. The room was too warm. She was glad when Miss Singer asked her to take a report to the principal's office. She ran all the way down the cool hall.

On the way back she walked more slowly. Running had given her a sharp pain in her side. The room seemed even warmer, and the noise of the children louder and louder. Candita was as tired as if she had run a race.

She put her head on her folded arms on her desk, and shut her eyes. The pain in her side was beginning again. It was suddenly sharper and more important than any other thing. It was as if it had always been there. She could not remember a time when there had not been a pain in her side.

Someone put a hand lightly on her shoulder. "Candita, are you asleep?"

She shook her head slowly.

It was Miss Singer, and it was a good thing that she was speaking Spanish. "Does something hurt?"

"Yes," she answered in Spanish, too. "Something hurts here." She put her hand to her side and said, "I would like to go home."

"Can you stand up?" Miss Singer asked.

Candita tried to stand. Miss Singer held her hand tightly, but when she stood up, it was too much. The pain was too great and she sat down again.

"Sit quietly, then," said Miss Singer. "Put your head down again, Candita." Candita's head sank back on her arm. It seemed a long time before she heard Miss Singer's voice again.

"Someone went to your house, Candita, but no one is at home. We will take you to the hospital. We have left a note for your mother."

Soon someone lifted her gently and carried her downstairs and into an automobile.

Once a long time ago, when they had gone to San Juan in Puerto Rico, someone had taken her and Mama for a ride in an automobile. She wished she could keep her eyes open now and see the New York streets as she had seen the streets of San Juan, but the pain did not allow it.

She kept her eyes closed, and after the car stopped, again she was carried in strong arms.

"Candita, you are at the hospital now. They will see what is wrong and make you well. Soon your mother will come to see you."

A girl with serious dark eyes untied Candita's shoes and helped her into a bed. Now there was no longer pain. There was only deep sleep.

Much, much later, she dreamed that she was in Puerto Rico, reading the whole book of *Bushy Tail the Squirrel*. In her dream it seemed that she had never read it so well. Her mother's voice awakened her, "Candita, the appendix is out. The doctor says you will be well now."

Candita opened her eyes. Everything in the room seemed far away and shadowy. Candita took a deep breath. "It does not hurt any more, Mama," she said, and sighed deeply.

Mama nodded. "I can sleep this night, for I have seen you and I have heard you speak to me."

A girl in a faded blue uniform came when Candita's mother left. "Up to now," she said, "I've only seen you asleep. How are you feeling?"

"I think I am better. Thank you," Candita said, in English. She was speaking English!

"The nurse sent me here to keep you company. I'm a helper in the hospital. My name is Jeanie."

Candita said, "You are the one who took me to the room with the strong light, no?"

"Yes," Jeanie said. "I took you from there, too, after you had your appendix taken out. You told me a long story."

"I told you a story?"

"About Bushy Tail the Squirrel. It was as long as a book."

"It is a book."

"Do you learn every word in all the books you read?"

"It is the first I have read in English."

"The first? You told it as if you had known English all your life."

Candita held her breath and felt her heart begin to pound. It was as she had hoped. She could say anything she wanted to say—almost anything. It would be difficult to talk about some things, but she could try.

While she was in the hospital, Candita talked English as much as she could. And on the first day of school, she said to her friends in English, "I am glad to be back." She told them about the hospital.

When Miss Singer came into the room, she was carrying a white and pink cake. "It is so we can celebrate your return," she said in Spanish.

Linda stood up. "Miss Singer, Candita is no longer the shy one. She does not stop talking. And do you know which language she speaks?"

"Which?" asked Miss Singer.

"English!" said Linda. "No more Spanish. The hospital removed the Spanish language from Candita when they took out her appendix!"

Everyone burst into laughter.

Candita laughed, too. She said, "I can still speak Spanish, but today is the day for English."

Miss Singer was surprised. "It sounds fine, Candita—as if you were born in New York." It was just as she had dreamed, and better.

After lunch Candita cut the cake and everyone in the room celebrated.

"Come and visit me soon, Candita," Miss Singer told her as she left. "But do not come to this room tomorrow morning. You are ready for your true class now that you speak English."

Ancient Romans wrote on wax tablets. They scratched out mistakes by scraping the wax with a stylus. Our word **erase** comes from the Latin *erasus*. *Erasus* comes from a word which means "to scratch out."

"A" IS FOR APPLE

Our lives are very different from those of cave men. Suppose someone asked you to name the discovery, or development, that was most important in making this change possible. What would you tell him? The answer is as simple as A-B-C. In fact, that is the answer: **A-B-C.**

For many thousands of years man had no way of recording his undertakings. He passed his ideas on to his children by word of mouth. After a writing system was developed, people were able to leave records of their inventions and thoughts. Those who followed could study these records and pick up where the last inventor left off.

Of course man did not use an alphabet at first. When he first began to record his thoughts, he did so by drawing PICTURES. Usually they were of wild animals. We can still see these pictures on the walls of some caves.

Later, man combined several pictures to tell the story of an EVENT. Perhaps someone wanted to record what happened on a hunt. He might have drawn his picture like this:

Three men *crossed* the mountains *to hunt* deer.

After four days *they had* shot two deer.

We, too, can use this method of describing an event. Suppose you wanted to send a report of your birthday party to someone who could not read. One way you might do it is to draw a picture that shows yourself, a cake with candles, presents, and your friends.

These pictures really are not writing at all. The marks represent happenings, not language. There is an important difference between these pictures of events and written language. The pictures are not very exact.

One way you can test this is by asking friends to tell you what the pictures stand for. Everyone will get the idea, but no two people will tell the story in just the same words.

Another way you can test this is by trying to picture such feelings as love, hate, wonder, and excitement. It might be difficult to do.

Because picture drawing did not allow man to say things clearly, he kept working to improve his system of recording thoughts.

One of man's first steps in recording thoughts was to picture EVENTS. His next big step was to use pictures to stand for single WORDS.

Suppose someone wanted to say, "I saw one ox." He might represent it like this:

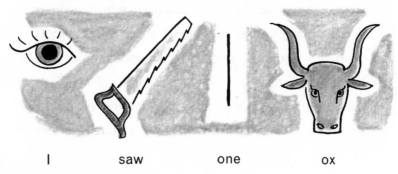

| I | saw | one | ox |

In this system you can see that a picture is a symbol for a word. It is a real writing system, for the marks represent language.

However, this kind of a writing system has a very big drawback. You would need to learn one symbol for every single word in your language. Think of all the thousands of symbols you would have to learn! You would never have enough, because languages are always adding new words, just as people are always learning new words.

The next step in written language was a very big one. Instead of using a picture to stand for a WHOLE word, each picture, or symbol, stood for a SYLLABLE of a word.

Let's play with a word in our own language. Of course our English words were not used because the early writings were in other languages. Using one of our English words, however, will show us how the system worked. Let us try to picture, in syllables, the word *forgive*.

The picturing of syllables is based on sound, not on meaning or spelling. The syllables *for*, *fore*, and *four* all sound the same. We can use the symbol 4 to represent all three, including the first syllable in the word *forgive*.

The second syllable *give* might be pictured by drawing a pair of outstretched hands.

Now the word *forgive* can be shown in this way:

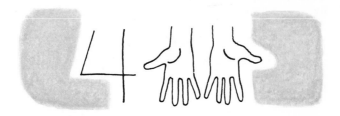

In the same way these words can be shown:

foursquare   forget   forehead

The development of syllable writing was important, because the symbols represented not whole WORDS but only COMBINATIONS OF SOUNDS.

Finally someone had a new idea. One symbol could stand for ONE SOUND. About 3,500 years ago the Phoenicians developed such an ALPHABET.

The Phoenicians were sailors and traders. When they visited the Greek cities, they left more than goods. They left their alphabet.

The Greeks adapted the Phoenician alphabet to suit the needs of their own language. They made several changes and added some symbols to make their own alphabet.

Later the Romans adapted the Greek symbols and arrived at *their* alphabet.

The English alphabet uses the Roman symbols, or letters, and has added the letters **J, U,** and **W.**

Let us study the development of the name and form of one letter—the letter **A.**

This was one of the early picture symbols. It meant *ox.*

As time passed this symbol was drawn less carefully.

The Phoenicians made the symbol the first letter of their alphabet. They called it ALEPH.

When the Greeks borrowed this Phoenician symbol, they changed its name to ALPHA.

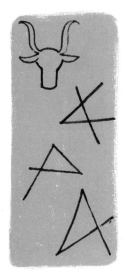

The Romans borrowed the Greek symbol, changed its name to AH, and gave it its present shape.

The English-speaking people kept the Roman symbol, but changed its name to **A**.

The word *alphabet* came from the Greek. The first letter of the Greek alphabet is ALPHA. The second letter is BETA. These two words, ALPHA and BETA, were combined to make our word *alphabet*.

Today one of the first books a child sees is usually an A-B-C book. It starts out, as you should remember, something like this:

And so it must have been from the beginning when early writers were teaching in a similar way —teaching not children, but grown men:

is for

is for

is for

Without a writing system, man's problems of record-keeping would be difficult, if not impossible. The alphabet is a wonderful invention. Whether we realize it or not, we THINK as well as WRITE with the words which are made from it. It is an important tool with which progress is made by man.

Signs of the Times

If you lived in a European city in the Middle Ages, your home might have been on "The Street of the Bear with a Hat On." The sign marking your street might look like this.

 Perhaps your father owned a dairy. The sign outside his place of business could look like this. Can you think of any other pictures for a dairy?

Why do you think these strange signs were used? Wouldn't it have been easier to put up a sign saying "Main Street," or write the word *Dairy* above the door as we do today?

Picture signs were necessary because so few people knew how to read in those days.

Many families used signs to mark their homes. A man by the name of Cox could use a sign with the picture of two cocks painted on it.

What did you learn in "**A** Is for Apple" that helps you understand this sign? Can you think of ways to picture other last names?

In one village, the schoolmaster put up a sign showing a man whipping a small boy with a birch twig. Everyone knew who lived at his address!

People whose names or business could not be pictured made up signs. The inns of the times are famous for their strange signs.

Hog in Armour

Cock and Anchor

Some businessmen hung the tools of their trades outside their shops. A broom told the public that this was the chimney sweep's store.

What would a large pair of scissors tell you? What about a boot? a meat cleaver? a hat?

Can you think of others?

E is the Escalator
   That gives an elegant ride.
You step on the stair
With an easy air
   And up and up you glide.
It's nicer than scaling ladders
   Or scrambling 'round a hill,
For you climb and climb
But all the time
   You're really standing still.

THE TALKING CAT

Long ago in Canada, there were no television sets or radios or movies. The people who lived in the country spent so much of their time working that they did not miss these things. But when they gathered in their kitchens in the long winter evenings, there was need for some kind of entertainment.

So anyone who could tell a good story was more than welcome as a guest. Michel Meloche was such a one. He was a runner of the woods, who spent most of his time trapping and working in the lumber camps. But on those rare occasions when he dropped in to visit friends and relatives, he turned their simple homes into enchanted theaters.

So, let's pretend that we are in a Canadian kitchen on a winter evening long ago. Outside the snow is deep and the wind is howling. A wolf adds his lonely howl to that of the wind. But in our cozy kitchen, the cookstove is red from the crackling fire.

Suddenly all the French voices that go so fast and sound so excited no matter what they are saying become silent. Michel has risen from his bench by the fire and clapped his pipe over the woodbox. Around his waist he wears a long red sash, brighter than the flame in the stove, and his blue eyes seem to be remembering strange and wonderful sights. Michel begins his story of Tante Odette and Chouchou.

Once, my friends, a great change came into Tante Odette's life. It all happened because of a change that came over Chouchou. This gray cat was a good pet because he seemed quite content to live on bread and vegetable soup. Tante Odette kept a pot of soup boiling on the back of the stove. She added a little more water and a few more vegetables to it each day. In this way, she always had soup on hand.

She baked her own bread in her outdoor oven once a week. If the bread grew hard before the week was up, she softened it in the soup. So nothing was ever thrown away.

As Tante Odette worked at her weaving every evening, Chouchou would lie by the stove and steadily stare at her with his big green eyes.

"If only you could talk," Tante Odette would say, "what company you would be for me."

One fall evening, Tante Odette was busy at her weaving. Her short fingers flew among the threads like pigeons.

Suddenly there was a knock at the door.

The old woman took the lamp from the table and went to the door. She opened it slowly. The light from the lamp fell on a queer old man who had the unmistakable look of the woods. He wore a bright red sash around his waist and a black crow feather in his woolen cap. He had a bushy moustache like a homemade broom and a sun-browned face.

"Pierre Leblanc," said the old man, making a deep bow.

"What do you want?" asked Tante Odette sharply.

"I'm looking for a place to stay and for work," answered Pierre Leblanc. "I am getting too old to trap for furs. I would like a job here."

"I don't need help," snapped Tante Odette. "I can do everything myself. And I have my cat."

She started to close the door, but the man put his hand against it. He was staring at Chouchou.

"A very smart cat he looks to be," he said. "Why don't you ask him if you should take me in? After all, you need pay me nothing but a roof over my head and a little food."

Tante Odette's eyes grew bigger.

"How silly," she said. "A cat can't talk. I only wish—"

To her great surprise, Chouchou began to talk.

"Oh, indeed I can," he told her, "if the matter is important enough. This Pierre Leblanc looks to me like a very fine man and a good worker. You should take him in."

Tante Odette stood with her mouth open for two minutes before she could make a sound. At last she said, "Then come in. It is so unusual for a cat to be able to talk that I'm sure one should listen to him when he does."

The old man walked close to the stove and stretched his fingers toward it. He looked at the pot of soup boiling on the back.

Chouchou spoke again.

"Pierre looks hungry," he said. "Offer him some soup—a big, deep bowl of it."

"Oh, my," sighed Tante Odette, "our soup won't last out the week. But if you say so, Chouchou."

Pierre sat at the wooden table and downed the soup like a starved wolf. When he had finished, Tante Odette pointed to the place where he would sleep. Then she took Chouchou on her lap.

"It is strange that you should begin talking after all these years. Whatever came over you?"

But Chouchou had nothing more to say. He covered his nose with the tip of his tail, and there was not another word out of him all night.

Tante Odette decided that the cat's advice had been good. No longer did she have to go to the barn and feed the beasts. Pierre was indeed a good worker. He seemed quite satisfied with his place to sleep and his bowls of vegetable soup and the bread.

Only Chouchou seemed to have grown dissatisfied since his arrival.

"Why do you feed Pierre nothing but soup and bread?" he asked one day. "A workingman needs more food than that. How about some headcheese and meat pie?"

Tante Odette was startled, but Pierre went on drinking his soup.

"But meat costs money," she told the cat.

"It is well worth it," said the cat. "Even I am getting a little tired of soup. A nice meat pie for dinner tomorrow would fill all the empty cracks inside me."

So when Pierre went out to the barn to water the beasts, Tante Odette lifted the lid of the chest, fished out a torn woolen sock and pulled a few coins out of it. She jumped in surprise when she raised her head and saw Pierre standing in the open doorway watching her.

"I forgot the pail," said Pierre. "I will draw some water from the well while I am about it."

The old woman quickly dropped the lid of the chest and got the pail from behind the stove.

"After Pierre has done his work," said Chouchou, "he will be glad to go to the store and buy the meat for you."

Tante Odette frowned at the cat.

"But I am the best shopper in the area," she said. "I can bring the old storekeeper down a few pennies on everything I buy."

"Pierre is a good shopper, too," said Chouchou. "In all Canada there is not a better judge of meat. Perhaps he will even see something that you would not have thought to buy. Send him to the store."

It turned out that the old man was just as good a shopper as Chouchou had said. He returned from the village with a pinkish piece of meat, a freshly dressed pig's head, a bag of candy and some tobacco for himself.

"But my money," said Tante Odette. "Did you spend all of it?"

"What is money for but to spend?" asked Chouchou from his place by the stove. "Can you eat money or smoke it in a pipe?"

"No," said Tante Odette.

"Can you put it over your shoulders to keep you warm?"

"No."

"Would it burn in a stove to cook your food?"

"Oh, no indeed!"

Chouchou closed his eyes.

"Then what good is money?" he asked. "The sooner one gets rid of it, the better."

Tante Odette's troubled face smoothed.

"I never saw it that way before," she agreed. "Of course, you are right, Chouchou. And you are right, too, Pierre, for choosing such fine food."

But when Pierre went out to get some vegetables, Tante Odette counted her coins again.

"I have a small fortune, Chouchou," she said. "Now tell me again why these coins are no good."

But Chouchou had nothing more to say.

One Tuesday when Pierre Leblanc was cutting trees in the woods and Tante Odette was baking bread in the outdoor oven, a stranger came riding down the road on a one-eyed horse. He stopped in front of the white fence. He jumped from his horse and went over to Tante Odette.

The old woman saw at once that he was a man of the woods. His cap was red. Matching it was the red sash tied around his waist. He looked very much like Pierre Leblanc.

"Can you tell me, Madame," he asked, "if a man named Pierre Leblanc works here?"

"Yes, he does," answered Tante Odette, "and a very good worker he is."

The stranger did not look satisfied.

"Of course, Canada is full of Pierre Leblancs," he said. "It is a very common name. Does this Pierre Leblanc wear a red sash like mine?"

"So he does," said Tante Odette.

"On the other hand, many Pierre Leblancs wear red sashes," said the man. "Does he have a moustache like a homemade broom?"

"Yes, indeed," said the woman.

"But there must be many Pierre Leblancs with red sashes and moustaches like brooms," continued the stranger. "This Pierre Leblanc who now works for you, can he throw his voice?"

"Throw his voice!" cried Tante Odette.

"Haven't you heard of such a thing?" asked the man. "But of course only a few can—probably only one Pierre Leblanc in a thousand. This

Pierre with you, can he throw his voice behind trees and in boxes and up on the roof so it sounds as if someone else is talking?"

"I wouldn't have such a one in my house," the woman cried. "He would be better company for the *loup-garou*, that evil one who can change into many shapes."

The man laughed heartily.

"My Pierre Leblanc could catch the *loup-garou* in a wolf trap and lead him around by the chain. He is that clever. That is why I am trying to find him. I want him to go trapping with me this winter. There have never been so many foxes. I need Pierre, for he is smarter than any fox."

The sound of wheels caused them both to turn around. Pierre Leblanc was driving the ox team from the woods. He stared at the man standing beside Tante Odette. The man stared back. Then both men ran and hugged each other.

"Good old Pierre!"

"Georges, my friend, where have you kept yourself all summer? How did you find me?"

Tante Odette left them yelling and hugging. She walked into the house with a worried look on her face. She sat down to her weaving. Finally she stopped and turned to Chouchou.

"I am a little dizzy, Chouchou," she said. "This *loup-garou* voice has upset me. What do you make of it all?"

Chouchou said nothing.

"Please tell me what to do," begged Tante Odette. "Shall we let him stay here? It would be very uncomfortable to have voices coming from the roof and the trees."

Chouchou said nothing.

"Is he maybe in league with the *loup-garou*?"

Chouchou said nothing. Tante Odette angrily threw a piece of wood at him.

"Where is your tongue?" she shouted. "Have you no words for me when I need them most?"

But if a cat will not speak, who has got his tongue?

Pierre Leblanc came walking in.

"Such a man!" he roared happily.

"Are you going away with him?" asked the woman, not knowing if she wanted him to say "yes" or "no." If only Chouchou hadn't been so stubborn.

"That is a problem," said Pierre. "If I go into the woods this winter, it will be cold and I will work like an ox. But there will be money in my pocket after the furs are sold. If I stay here, I will be warm and comfortable but—"

He pulled his pockets inside out. Nothing fell from them.

"What about your being able to throw your voice to other places?" asked Tante Odette.

"Did Georges say I could do that?"

Tante Odette nodded.

"Ha! Ha!" laughed Pierre. "What a joker he is!"

"But perhaps it is true," said the woman.

"If you really want to know," said Pierre, "ask Chouchou. He would not lie. Can I throw my voice, Chouchou?"

"Of course not!" he answered. "Whoever heard of such nonsense?"

Tante Odette sighed. Then she remembered that this did not fix everything.

"Will you go with him?" she asked Pierre. "I have made it very comfortable for you here. And now it is only for supper that we have soup."

Chouchou spoke up.

"Tante Odette, how can you expect such a good man as Pierre Leblanc to work for only food and room? If you would pay him a coin from time to time, he would be quite satisfied to stay."

"But I can't afford that," said the woman.

"Of course you can," said Chouchou. "You have a small fortune in the old sock in your chest. Remember what I told you about money?"

"Tell me again," said Tante Odette. "It is hard to hold on to such a thought for long."

"Money is to spend," repeated the cat. "Can it carry hay and water to the beasts? Can it cut down trees for firewood? Can it dig through the snow when winter comes?"

"I have caught it again," said Tante Odette. "If you will stay with me, Pierre, I will pay you a coin from time to time."

Pierre smiled and bowed.

"I shall be happy to stay here with you and your wise cat," he decided. "Now I will unload my wood and put it in a neat pile by the door."

He stamped out. Tante Odette sat down at her weaving again.

"We have made a good bargain, haven't we, Chouchou?" She smiled contentedly.

But Chouchou said nothing.

That is the way it was, my friends. It would have been a different story if Pierre had not been such a good worker. So, remember this: If you must follow the advice of a talking cat, be sure you know who is doing the talking for him.

LOUIS BRAILLE

Louis Braille felt the warm sun on his face, and breathed deeply. The air was full of the sweet smell of flowers. *How nice to be back in the country again*, he thought. He turned around. Slowly he felt his way up a few stone steps. Now he sniffed the familiar smell of leather. Sighing, he sat down in the doorway of his father's harness shop. Footsteps sounded behind him.

"Ah, Louis, how will you spend your time this summer?"

The boy raised his face toward his father's voice. "Thinking, Father, thinking," he replied.

"And have they given you much to think about at school?"

"Yes, Father," Louis answered, "listening and thinking are the main things we do. We must remember what our teacher tells us for there are very few books for us to read."

His father sat down. "Tell me about it, Louis. How can they teach blind boys to read?"

For an hour Louis described the history of the school and its teaching methods. Louis was one of the few blind children at the time who could go to school. There was just one school for the sightless in France. Usually only children of the rich could afford to go there, but Mr. Braille had saved enough money to send his son. Still very little was known about the school.

Louis told his father that the school had been the idea of a man named Haüy. Haüy had been upset by the sight of blind people begging in the streets. He thought they might have a better life if only there were some way they could learn to read. Haüy worked out a method of sorts, and in 1784 he opened his school.

At first he made the letters of the alphabet out of sticks. The sticks, each six inches high, were put on a frame. In order to spell out one sentence the frame had to be so big it covered one whole side of the room. The children tapped their way to the frame. Then walking along, they ran their fingers over the sticks. Slowly they spelled out the words.

After a while Haüy replaced the slow stick method with a better one. The letters of the alphabet, now only one inch high, were pressed on cardboard. The letters stood out so that a person could feel them. The large pieces of cardboard were put between covers in book form. When Louis entered the school, there were three such books. Each book was made up of twenty parts. Each part weighed twenty pounds! Since they were so big and took so long to make, they cost a lot of money.

"What we need, Father," Louis explained, "is an alphabet that is different from the one used by the sighted. The letters should be read with the fingertips. We must have more books—libraries of books! We must be able to make the books smaller and for less money."

"Perhaps, my son, you will work out such an alphabet. Doing that for the blind may be what life has in store for you. But come, now you can help me make a fringe for this harness." So saying, his father led Louis into the workshop.

Each day when Louis finished working on the fringes, he would ask his father for a few scraps of leather. As he sat in the doorway, he would begin to cut the leather. *Perhaps*, he thought, *a circle could stand for the letter A, a square for the letter B.* But he found that too many shapes were needed for all the letters. And you certainly couldn't write that way.

All summer Louis tried many different methods, but nothing seemed to work. It was a discouraged boy who returned to school in the fall.

Shortly after classes began, Louis and his classmates were called to the meeting hall. There must be some important news! Low murmurings filled the room as the boys wondered about it. Then, at the first sound of the director's footsteps, they became suddenly quiet.

"I have here," the director began, "some cards which I will pass among you. Run your fingers over them."

The boys did as they were told. They could feel many little bumps and lines. The shapes meant nothing to them. Puzzled faces turned toward the director's voice.

"I will explain the meaning of the marks," he went on. "An army captain brought these cards to me last summer. He told me that he had found it hard to give orders to his men at night. If he spoke, the enemy could hear him. If he wrote the orders, the men needed a light to read by. The light, like the voice, told the enemy where they were. A new method of giving orders was needed.

"The captain had developed a system of punched dots and dashes. The men could run

their fingers over the card and feel the marks. Several long dashes might mean that they should move forward. A circle of dots might mean that the enemy had surrounded them. All the men needed to do was learn the code. The system worked quite well for him. He thought you, too, might find it useful."

Louis' face beamed with understanding. This was what he had been looking for! Here was a kind of writing different from that used by the sighted. He wanted to shout for joy!

Louis quickly learned the code. Yet as he worked with it he realized the system would not solve the problems of the blind. It was based on sounds instead of letters. Each group of dots and dashes stood for a certain sound, but there were too many marks for each sound—as many as twelve. It was better than Haüy's letter system because it could be written. Still the writing was slow and took up too much space. Besides, the dashes were hard to make. An easier method was needed, but Louis now had an idea. Dots! An alphabet made up of dots!

During the day Louis went to his classes. At night he often sat up thinking about the dots. A pointed stylus was his tool for punching holes. Often he punched steadily all night until he heard the sound of street wagons. Only then did he remember to get a bit of sleep.

Nights without sleep had made him weak and pale. His throat ached and he had a bad cough. The cold school building didn't help either. With the coming of summer he returned to his home in the country. The fresh air made him feel better. Once again he sat in the doorway of his father's harness shop.

Each day Louis fingered the pieces of leather. Now instead of cutting squares and circles, he punched holes in the leather with an awl. The awl was like a very sharp stylus. He worked slowly and carefully. He didn't want the awl to slip again as it had when he was three years old.

Neighbors passing by saw the boy punching holes day in and day out. "Good day, Louis," they would sing out. "Still pricking the leather?"

"Yes, but I'm now on the fringe of success," he would call back.

Fall came and school opened again. Louis had made much progress on his alphabet code. He was eager now to explain it to the director.

"I'll help you all I can, Louis," he promised. "However, there may be a long delay before your code system is accepted. Many people do not accept changes quickly."

Indeed it was not until two years after Louis' death that his code was accepted as the official method of reading and writing for the blind. The cough which had always been with him took his life early. Yet while he lived, he worked to improve his code system. Today the system, named after him, is called "braille," and is used all over the world.

At the age of three, a sharp awl had blinded Louis Braille. At the age of fifteen a dull awl had given him a way to see. Today his wish has come true. There are now books—whole libraries of books—for the blind.

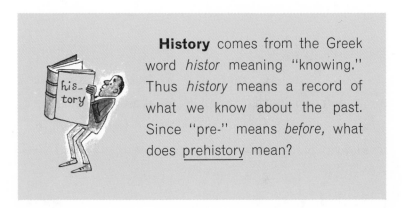

History comes from the Greek word *histor* meaning "knowing." Thus *history* means a record of what we know about the past. Since "pre-" means *before,* what does prehistory mean?

Pinched for Time

Jim *itched* to get outside. He wanted to *water* the farm animals before the guests arrived for his party. He had promised his father that he would *turn over a new leaf* and do his chores on time. Since he didn't want to have to *eat his words*, he was determined *not to let any grass grow under his feet.*

His mother's fingers *flew among the threads* and at last the buttons were on his coat. He *drew a deep breath*, put the coat on, and was outside in *the twinkling of an eye.*

When the last chore was done, Jim returned to the house *walking on air.* His dad's praise for the quick work would *be music to his ears.*

Five minutes later Jim *laid eyes on* the first of his visitors.

1. sewed quickly
2. make him feel good
3. give a drink to
4. a very short time
5. sighed with relief
6. saw
7. begin to do better
8. was in a hurry
9. to work quickly
10. feeling very happy
11. take back what he said

AMELIA BEDELIA

"Oh, Amelia Bedelia, your first day of work. And I can't be here. But I made a list for you. You do just what the list says," said Mrs. Rogers.

Mrs. Rogers got into the car with Mr. Rogers. They drove away.

"My, what nice folks. I'm going to like working here," said Amelia Bedelia.

Amelia Bedelia went inside. "Such a grand house. These must be rich folks. But I must get to work. Here I stand just looking. And me with a whole list of things to do." Amelia Bedelia stood there a minute longer. "I think I'll make a surprise for them. I'll make a lemon-meringue pie. I do make good pies."

So Amelia Bedelia went into the kitchen. She put a little of this and some of that into a bowl. She mixed and she rolled. Soon her pie was ready to go into the oven.

"There," said Amelia Bedelia. "That's done. Now let's see what this list says." Amelia Bedelia read,

Change the towels in the green bathroom.

Amelia Bedelia found the green bathroom. "Those towels are very nice. Why change them?" she thought. Then Amelia Bedelia remembered what Mrs. Rogers had said. She must do just what the list told her. "Well, all right," said Amelia Bedelia.

Amelia Bedelia got some scissors. She cut a little here and a little there. And she changed those towels. "There," said Amelia Bedelia.

She looked at her list again.

Dust the furniture.

"Did you ever hear tell of such a silly thing. At my house we undust the furniture. But to each his own way."

Amelia Bedelia took one last look at the bathroom. She saw a big box with the words *Dusting*

Powder on it. "Well, look at that. A special powder to dust with!" exclaimed Amelia Bedelia. So Amelia Bedelia dusted the furniture. "That should be dusty enough. My, how nice it smells."

Amelia Bedelia read,

Draw the drapes when the sun comes in.

She looked up. The sun was coming in. Amelia Bedelia looked at the list again. "Draw the drapes? That's what it says. I'm not much of a hand at drawing, but I'll try." So Amelia Bedelia sat right down and she drew those drapes. Amelia Bedelia marked off about the drapes.

"Now what?"

Put the lights out when you finish in the living room.

Amelia Bedelia thought about this a minute. She turned off the lights. Then she carefully unscrewed each bulb. And Amelia Bedelia put the

lights out. "So those things need to be aired out, too. Just like blankets and babies. Oh, I do have a lot to learn."

"My pie!" exclaimed Amelia Bedelia. She hurried to the kitchen. "Just right," she said. She took the pie out of the oven and put it on the table to cool.

Then she looked at the list.

Measure two cups of rice.

"That's next," said Amelia Bedelia. Amelia Bedelia found two cups. She filled them with rice. And Amelia Bedelia measured that rice. Amelia Bedelia laughed. "These folks do want me to do funny things." Then she poured the rice back into the container.

The meat market will deliver a steak and a chicken. Please trim the fat before you put the steak in the icebox. And please dress the chicken.

When the meat arrived, Amelia Bedelia opened the bag. She looked at the steak for a long time. "Yes," she said. "That will do nicely." Amelia Bedelia got some lace and bits of ribbon. And Amelia Bedelia trimmed that fat before she put the steak in the icebox.

199

"Now I must dress the chicken. I wonder if she wants a he chicken or a she chicken?" said Amelia Bedelia. Amelia Bedelia went right to work. Soon the chicken was finished.

Amelia Bedelia heard the door open. "The folks are back," she said. She rushed out to meet them.

"Amelia Bedelia, why are all the light bulbs outside?" asked Mr. Rogers.

"The list just said to put the lights out," said Amelia Bedelia. "It didn't say to bring them back in. Oh, I do hope they didn't get aired too long."

"Amelia Bedelia, the sun will fade the furniture. I asked you to draw the drapes," said Mrs. Rogers.

"I did! I did! See," said Amelia Bedelia. She held up her picture.

Then Mrs. Rogers saw the furniture. "The furniture!" she cried.

"Did I dust it well enough?" asked Amelia Bedelia. "That's such nice dusting powder."

Mr. Rogers went to wash his hands. "I say," he called. "These are very unusual towels."

Mrs. Rogers dashed into the bathroom. "Oh, my best towels," she said.

"Didn't I change them enough?" asked Amelia Bedelia.

Mrs. Rogers went to the kitchen. "I'll cook the dinner. Where is the rice I asked you to measure?"

"I put it back in the container. But I remember—it measured four and a half inches," said Amelia Bedelia.

"Was the meat delivered?" asked Mrs. Rogers.

"Yes," said Amelia Bedelia. "I trimmed the fat just like you said. It does look nice."

Mrs. Rogers rushed to the icebox. She opened it. "Lace! Ribbons! Oh, dear!" said Mrs. Rogers.

"The chicken—you dressed the chicken?" asked Mrs. Rogers.

"Yes, and I found the nicest box to put him in," said Amelia Bedelia.

"Box!" exclaimed Mrs. Rogers. Mrs. Rogers hurried over to the box. She lifted the lid. There lay the chicken. And he was just as dressed as he could be.

Mrs. Rogers was angry. She was very angry. She opened her mouth. Mrs. Rogers meant to tell Amelia Bedelia she was fired. But before she could get the words out, Mr. Rogers put something in her mouth. It was so good Mrs. Rogers forgot about being angry.

"Lemon-meringue pie!" she exclaimed.

"I made it to surprise you," said Amelia Bedelia happily.

So right then and there Mr. and Mrs. Rogers decided that Amelia Bedelia must stay. And so she did. Mrs. Rogers learned to say undust the furniture, unlight the lights, close the drapes, and things like that. Mr. Rogers didn't care if Amelia Bedelia trimmed all of his steaks with lace. All he cared about was having her there to make lemon-meringue pie.

Limericks

There once was a Prince, tall and handsome,
Who was held by some crooks for a ransom.
One day, through a hole
He quietly stole
And then he took off and he ran some!

A high-flying witch named old Zoomwick
Was grounded because she got airsick.
It seemed that her plight
As she flew through the night
Was due to a twitch in her broomstick!

These five-line nonsense verses are called limericks. No one is certain who made up the first limerick. It is not even known for sure in which country the first limericks were written. But this kind of verse is named for a town in Ireland by the same name.

There once was a small boy named Edward,
Who hated at night to go bedward,
'Til his father did land
With the flat of a hand
On the opposite end from his headward!

The rhyme in limericks is often achieved by the use of "coined" or "made up" words like *bedward* and *headward* in the poem you just read.

Have you noticed a sing-song rhythm in the words of these limericks as you read them? Do you think you could write a limerick? Why not try? Don't be discouraged if your first limericks aren't very funny. Here's a verse about someone who had a hard time writing limericks.

There once was a poet named Crandom
Who wrote limericks strictly at random.
But all of his verse
Went from bad to worse
'Til people no longer could stand 'em.

This picture may give you an idea for your own limerick.

BRANDS

In the days when there were no fences in the West, the best means of identifying cattle was to brand them with a hot iron. Even today, when much of the land in the West is still open range, the only way of sorting the cattle of one ranch from those of another is through the brands. During the spring and summer, the cattle of many ranchers graze on the open range. When fall comes, cowboys from these ranches round them up and sort them according to the brands.

The act of branding hurts the young calves at the time, but the pain is very brief. Once the mark or brand is made, it never disappears. The brand cannot be rubbed or washed off. It is a permanent mark of ownership.

In the United States, the first people to use cattle brands were the Spaniards who explored the West long before this country was a nation. Spanish brands were very complicated and rich in design.

American cowboys and pioneers learned about brands from the Spaniards and Mexicans. The pioneers saw the need for brands. But instead of the fancy brands of Spain, the cowboys and pioneers made their brands simple and direct because they were easier to make, easier to remember, and easier to read.

How to Read a Brand

To a cowboy, each brand is simple to read, but a beginner can make many mistakes.

There are rules for reading cattle brands, just as there are rules for reading words. You are reading these words from left to right. If you tried reading them from right to left, they would not make sense. And if you tried spelling them from right to left, they would make even less sense. The words "real cowboy" would appear as "yobwoc laer"!

There are three rules for the reading of brands. They are read:

(1) from left to right;
(2) from top to bottom;
(3) from the outside to the inside.

Circle Bar X

Reading Single Letters

There are many different ways of making even a single letter.

Take the letter *R*. Standing upright, it is read as plain *R* and nothing else.

But the cowboy does things to letters and, in changing them, makes his own alphabet.

When he brands the letter *R* lying on its back, he calls it Lazy R. (It may face in either direction.)

If he stands *R* on its head, also facing in either direction, he calls it Crazy R.

When he puts feet on it, he calls it Walking R.

And wings on the letter make it a Flying R.

This figure, which the cowboy calls a Rocking R, is all one figure. The letter is rocking on a quarter circle.

By joining the quarter circle to the top of the *R*, the cowboy makes a Swinging R.

When the quarter circle is not joined to the *R*, the brand is read from top to bottom. This brand is an R Quarter Circle.

The letter *O* is always called *circle* and not *O*. It is one of the cowboys' favorite brands.

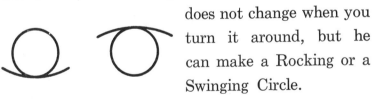

Circle X   Circle M   Circle Lazy L

The cowboy has fun with the circle brand, just as he does with other letters. He cannot make it into a Lazy or a Crazy Circle, because the circle

does not change when you turn it around, but he can make a Rocking or a Swinging Circle.

There is one thing he can do to the Circle brand which he cannot do to any of the other brands. He can mash it down. He calls this a Goose Egg.

There are one or two more things about cowboys' letters which you probably have already discovered for yourself.

First, all letters are capitals. There are no small letters in the cowboys' alphabet. In all the brands you have seen and read so far, there have been no small letters. The cowboys could have used them if they had wanted to, but they had a very good reason for using capitals instead. They are big and easy to read from a distance and they make good designs.

Second, some letters can do certain things which other letters cannot do. There is no rule here which you can follow. It is simply a matter of horse sense. Try to make a Walking I or a Walking T or a Walking L. It cannot be done, because they are not two-legged letters like *A*, *R*, *K*, *M*, and *N*.

210

Also, the cowboy does not use a Lazy I because it would look too much like a Bar.

Some letters cannot be crazy. As soon as an *M* stands on its head, it becomes a *W*, and a *W* becomes an *M*. If an *H* or an *I* or an *X* stands on its head, nothing happens. Upside down or right side up, these letters look the same.

Reading Numerals

Cowboys use numerals in brands, too. The numerals may stand alone or they may be combined with other numerals or with picture and letters.

Here are some brands which use numerals:

Lazy Two   Rocking Six   Seven Bar X

Because the numeral 1 can be mixed up with the letter I, cowboys are careful to brand each of them clearly.

And brands with two numerals can be made in the same way that you would usually write the numerals, and they are read in the same way.

Sometimes cowboys join two numerals to make a single design instead of having each of the numerals stand alone.

Sixty-three   Ninety-six   Forty-six

Picture Brands

Cowboys like picture brands. A rancher might be very proud of his home and so choose the Cabin or the House brand.

A cowboy living on Hat Creek might use a brand which would be both an address and a brand.

Cowboys also make designs of the things they see around their ranches and use them as brands.

Horse Track   Three Snakes   Pitchfork

Picture brands usually are used alone, but sometimes they are used in designs with letters and numerals.

A Pitchfork L makes a very good design.

A rancher might want the Three Bells brand. Instead of branding all three bells, he would put the numeral *3* before a bell.

213

Cowboys Remember

Never use more than three figures. Cowhide is worth money. The bigger the brand, the more hide is burned away. Also, a brand of more than three figures is difficult to read.

Use an "open" design that can be stamped clearly. A design in which the parts are crowded together will burn away too much hide and run together in places.

Open

Closed

Not only is the "closed" brand above too crowded, but it breaks one of the rules for designing a brand. It uses more than three figures.

A cattle brand, then, is usually made up of forms of letters, numerals, pictures, or a combination of these symbols. A cowboy makes sure that whatever symbol he chooses will make a good design and will be easy to read.

Cowboy brands, a form of picture writing, are a part of the cattle ranchers' language. As such, they are a part of the history of the West.

214

Unit Four

Highways and Byways

Word Meanings

Here are some words from "Highways and By-ways" and their meanings. These meanings should help you understand the words when they are used in the sentences which follow.

fam ine (fam′ən), a time of starving; lack of food
pre cious (presh′əs), valuable; worth much
seep (sēp), leak; ooze; trickle
sou ve nir (sü′və nēr′), keepsake; something to remind one of a place, event, or person
trudge (truj), walk with effort; walk wearily
wis dom (wiz′dəm), knowledge and good judgment based on experience; being wise

A famine is often caused by bad weather or insects destroying a country's crops.

Janet hoped that the old jewelry she had found in the attic was precious.

Rain seeped through a hole in the roof.

When Jane couldn't lift her suitcase, she decided that collecting rocks as vacation souvenirs wasn't such a good idea after all.

Jack trudged three miles through deep snow.

It's said that wisdom comes with age.

BALLS OF CLAY

Bobby Grant ran out of the breakers and flopped down breathlessly on the warm Florida sand next to his cousin, Tom.

"Boy, you're lucky to live around here, Tom," he said. "The swimming's great!"

"Sure, but you have lots of lakes in Minnesota, don't you?" his cousin asked.

"True, but you can't go for a swim in March— not unless you want to turn into an iceberg. That's why I was so glad my family decided to visit yours during spring vacation. I can't wait until everyone at home sees my tan!"

"Tan? What tan?" and Tom at once began to bury Bobby's legs in the sand.

"Ha! I'll get one yet," Bobby laughed.

Although Florida was crowded with vacationers at this time of year, Tom and Bobby were almost alone on this part of the beach. There were mostly private homes along this particular strip. One of them belonged to Bobby's uncle, Tom's dad, who had just moved to Florida with his family.

Tom had found the area most interesting. The beach in front of his house was quite sandy, and it was full of unusual shells, pieces of driftwood, and bits of wreckage from ships. Tom had already begun a collection of odds and ends, and he found new surprises every day. One of the pieces of driftwood had such an interesting shape that Tom, with the help of his dad, had made it into the base of a lamp for Tom's room.

Up the beach a little way, around by the bay, were some low cliffs. Tom had wandered over there several times, but he knew it would be even more fun to explore the area with a friend. He suggested this now to his cousin, Bob, who was quick to sense the excitement of such a venture.

"Say," Bob said eagerly, "just before vacation I was reading a library book on pirate treasure. There's supposed to be a lot of it still hidden in parts of Florida. Those cliffs over there might have good hiding places."

"I don't know about the buried treasure," Tom laughed. "If people haven't found it by now, I don't suppose we'd have much of a chance. But let's investigate."

Bobby pulled his legs out of the sand and stood up. After the warm sand the breeze felt cool. He reached down for his jacket and tossed it over his shoulders. "Race you!" he called, and the two boys dashed off down the beach.

Nearing the first cliff they slowed their pace. Bobby, the taller of the two boys, arrived first and began to climb. Tom was not far behind. Part way up the low cliff, Bobby stopped to catch his breath. He looked around. As he did so, something caught his eye. It looked like a small cave just over to his right. Tom stood next to him now, and Bobby spoke in a low, excited voice. "Have you noticed that cave before, Tom?"

Tom laughed. "Cave! Why, that's just a hole! It's the first time I've seen it, but I've never climbed this part before. Anyway, I don't think a pirate would bury a treasure chest in there."

"You never know," Bobby shrugged his shoulders. "I'm going to have a look."

Bobby and Tom made their way over to the "cave." It really was a hole. They had to look in one at a time. First Bobby peered into the opening. He couldn't see much in the darkness, but he could tell that there was a passage that ran several feet back into the ledge. The hole wasn't big enough for a boy to crawl into; still something could be hidden in it.

Carefully Bobby reached in. With his hand he explored the corners to see if anything had been

tucked far back. He was about to mutter his disappointment when, sure enough, his hand touched something. He didn't know what it was, but it felt like marbles or birds' eggs. There seemed to be a little pile of them. He picked up a handful and brought them out into the light.

"What do you think these are?" he showed the mysterious balls to Tom. They ranged from about the size of a large pea to almost the size of a golf ball. They were round and smooth and seemed to be made of hard clay.

"They look like clay balls to me," Tom said. "Anyway, they can't be worth anything."

"Guess you're right," Bobby sighed, but he dropped the balls into his pocket just the same.

Now it was Tom's turn to peer into the dark hole. He felt around in all the corners, but only brought forth more clay balls. He dropped a dozen or so in Bob's jacket pocket, since he hadn't brought his own. Then, for no particular reason, he gathered another handful.

The sky suddenly darkened. Tom looked up. "Looks like we're going to get some rain," he said. "Guess we'd better be heading back."

The two boys scrambled down the cliff to the sandy shore below. As they walked along the beach they began to toss the clay balls at floating driftwood. Sometimes they stopped for a moment to see if a ball could be made to skip over the surface of the ocean. By the time they neared their own beach area, the clay balls were gone and a few raindrops had begun to fall. The boys, hungry from the afternoon's exertions, turned and sped toward the house.

At the end of the week a well-tanned Bobby returned to Minnesota with his family. As he was unpacking his suitcase, a small clay ball rolled out of his jacket pocket. *Looks like I didn't toss them all away at that,* he grinned to himself. And he tucked it away in his dresser drawer with his other souvenirs from Florida.

One day about a week later, Bobby trudged home from school through the light snow that still remained on the ground. He closed the door behind him and then stopped to listen. It sounded as if his father was home already. Then a strange voice reached his ears. He hung up his coat and peered into the living room.

"Come on in, Son," his father called. "I want you to meet a friend of mine. This is Mr. King. He manages a museum in Cincinnati."

"How do you do, sir?" Bobby smiled politely.

"Oh, just fine!" Mr. King's hearty voice roared out. "You know, you look just as your dad did when I knew him in school. Of course you're a bit tanner, but you still look like a Grant."

"Yes, sir, we just returned from Florida." Bobby explained.

"So your father told me. Did you bring back any pirate treasure? We're always looking for some of it to put in our museum," said Mr. King shaking with laughter.

"Just some shells and a few pieces of driftwood," Bobby said. Then, as an afterthought, he added,

"Oh, and a clay ball—but no treasure. Guess the pirates . . ."

"Clay ball?" Mr. King interrupted him. "Sounds interesting. May I see it?"

Bobby looked at him in surprise. He couldn't imagine why anyone should want to see an old clay ball, but he went up to get it just the same.

Returning to the living room, he handed the tiny souvenir to Mr. King. "My cousin Tom and I found a lot of these in a hole in a cliff," he explained. "We figured they weren't worth anything so we tossed them away—all except this little one. I found it in my jacket pocket."

"Hm," Mr. King studied the clay ball. "Oh, it just couldn't be." He spoke more to himself than to the others.

"Couldn't be what, sir?" Bobby asked.

"Oh, it was only a thought," Mr. King fingered the ball as he spoke. "But it IS a possibility." And he went on to tell the Grants about a little-known form of pirate treasure.

Mr. King explained that some pirates used to hide precious stones in round clay balls and then pile them in caves. The pirates could find them again easily. If other people found them, very few would think to crack one open. "What do you say,

225

Bobby? Shall we take a look inside this ball?" And an eager Bobby sped up the stairs to get his knife.

On the way down Bobby met his mother coming out of the kitchen. "Wash your hands, Son, dinner is ready."

"But, Mom!" Bobby began, scraping his feet on the floor.

"No 'Buts,' young man, we have company, you know." And a very impatient Bobby stumbled back up the stairs.

Bobby couldn't help wiggling a bit all during dinner. He couldn't even keep his mind on the wonderful taste of the roast beef and mashed potatoes. He was eating too fast. Still when Mr. King began talking about pirates, Bobby became so interested that he almost forgot about his apple pie. Then he quickly swallowed that.

At last everyone moved into the living room. Bobby handed the knife to Mr. King and the visitor began scraping away. For what seemed like a very long time there was nothing but clay. Then—the ball cracked. Out rolled a small but shiny stone. Mr. King held it up to the light. Indeed it did glisten!

"W-what is it, Mr. King?" Bobby asked, and then held his breath waiting for an answer.

"Well, son, it will have to be tested, but it SEEMS to be a perfect blue-white diamond! Looks as if you might have found and lost a fortune at the young age of ten!" Mr. King's forceful voice resounded through the room.

Bobby gasped. He turned and raced back up the stairs. His hands scrambled through his desk drawer to find a pen and a piece of note paper. He began to write.

Dear Tom,

Guess what! We really did find pirate treasure in the cliff that day. Inside those clay balls are diamonds and other precious stones. Really!

As soon as you can, run back to our cave and see if there are any more clay balls in there. If there are, be sure to collect all of them.

I'll write again just as soon as I find out what we should do with them.

Here's hoping!

Your cousin,
"Blackbeard II" Grant

Bobby leaned back and stretched his arms. Then he folded his hands behind his head. He gazed out the window, with a dreamy look on his face. He began to plan what he would do with his part of the new-found fortune—IF!

When knights in Old England went to battle, they wore a coat of mail or metal armor. This coat of mail was called a *jack*. A **jacket**, then, was a "little coat of mail."

THE RISE OF THE ROADS

Suppose you awakened one morning to discover that all the bicycles, buses, cars, cabs, trains, wagons, and every other moving vehicle on wheels had disappeared. Not only that, but all the roads were gone, too. This would mean that all movement on the land, except by foot or animal, would now be stopped. Can you imagine what would happen to our way of life?

Roads and streets form a large network joining neighborhoods, cities, states, and even countries. We travel on roads so often that we take them for granted. Few of us ever think about how important roads are, or wonder how they came to be. Yet without them, we could not live as we do today.

Trails, the ancestors of the road, were made long before roads were built. Actually wild animals had as great a part in the making of trails as did man.

In the early Stone Age, about 20,000 years ago, both man and animals made trails simply by following a path that led from a cave or sleeping place to a water hole or hunting ground. Of course, these paths followed the easiest route. The route was often the long way around, because men and animals stayed away from steep hills and swamps whenever they could. At this time men were hunters and didn't stay long in any one area. Therefore, the paths did not become very deep.

As time went on the second step toward road building was taken. People left the wandering life and began to settle down in villages. They raised their own food and learned to make pottery and to weave cloth. Often they needed things they couldn't get in their own villages, so they began to trade goods with the people of other villages. They began to tame and train animals, such as the ox, to carry their loads for them. The continuous travel of men and animals over the same ground, to and from their neighboring villages, left deep tracks.

It has been said that the vehicle creates the road. This seems to be true for there were no roads with prepared surfaces until the wheel was invented about 5,500 years ago. People found it difficult to pull wagons over bumpy, muddy ground. To make a smoother surface, branches, sticks, and logs were put on the tracks. At last man was trying to improve the surface over which he moved.

The next step in road building was to pave the surface. The first paved roads were built about 4,000 years ago. In parts of Europe short stretches of ground were covered with stone blocks and, in some cases, bricks.

Now that people were using animals and vehicles to carry their loads, they began to travel farther and farther from home to trade their goods. Between villages they followed the roads. Between countries they followed trade routes.[1]

One of the longest and oldest of the trade routes is called the Old Silk Trade Route. It joins Asia with Europe and has been in use for over 2,000

[1] Roads and trade routes were sometimes marked by piling stones every so often. Through a forest they were often marked by blazing, or cutting, some bark from trees along the way. From this we get the expression, "blazing a trail."

years! As its name suggests, traders traveled over it to trade silk and other goods. The Old Silk Trade Route runs over 6,000 miles. Even today this route is still traveled, but a real road covers only a small part of it.

People of early civilizations built roads of a sort, but the first good road builders were the Romans. They built the first network of hard-surfaced roads. The Romans began their road building about 300 B.C. and continued for about five hundred years.

Roman roads were good because the people knew how to lay a solid, thick base. On top of this they put a pavement of flat stones. Their roads were a bit higher in the center than on the sides. Along the sides ran ditches so that the water could run off. These roads were also famous for their straightness. They went over most of the hills instead of around them.

The Roman roads were used mainly by soldiers. At first these roads went just through Italy. Then, as the Roman Empire spread, roads were built in other countries of Europe. In all they laid about 50,000 miles of roads. Some parts of the Roman roads are still in use.

The building of the Appian Way, one of the most famous of the Roman roads, was begun in 312 B.C.[2] It ran southeast of Rome. The Appian Way was narrow near the city, but parts of it were as wide as a three-lane highway. Since cemeteries were not allowed in Rome, it was the custom to build tombs along the roads leading from the city. The Appian Way was famous for its tombs, but they made it

[2] The Appian Way was begun by and named for a high Roman official, Appius Claudius Caecus. Often roads were named for the person who sponsored them.

impossible for later Roman road builders to widen the old road. Today one may still travel on sections of the Appian Way.

After the fall of the Roman Empire, Europe entered a period in history called the Middle Ages. It lasted from about the year 400 to about the year 1400. During this period many of the Roman roads fell to pieces and few new roads were built.

In the Middle Ages, most of the traveling was done by knights and fighting men who rode horseback. It was at this time that men began traveling on only one side of the road.

Often a group of knights saw other horsemen approaching along the highway.[3] No one could be sure if the approaching men were friends or enemies. If they were enemies, swordplay followed. Since most people held their swords in their right hand, the men would meet sword hand to sword hand. Therefore, when riders passed each other, they did so on the left. It was for this reason that the English, and people in some other parts of the world, began traveling on the left side of the road.[4]

In the Middle Ages few people, other than knights and fighting men, did much traveling. Since highwaymen, or robbers, often lay in wait near the roads, it was neither comfortable nor safe to travel.[5]

Even after the Middle Ages roads in Europe remained in poor shape for a while. They were one mudhole after another. In fact, smooth roads were not seen until the 1600's in England.

[3] In England *highways* were main roads that were higher than the ground around them. The King's men protected these roads. All travelers could use them. Private roads were called *byways*.

[4] Today one would not encounter swordplay on the highways, but the custom of moving on the left side of the road still remains in some countries.

[5] The word *travel* comes from the English word *travail*, which means "hard, painful work."

The man who did the most for road building in Europe was John McAdam.[6] By about 1851 he had developed a system of road building which made him famous. It was better than earlier methods because it was quick and did not cost too much. On top of a dirt base he put a layer of small stones. Traffic was allowed to pass over it until the stones were pressed together. Then a second layer of small stones was put down. These roads became so well known that they were called simply "macadam" roads. Macadam roads are still used in many parts of the world.

When the Europeans began improving their roads, they had the remains of the old Roman roads with which to work. On the other hand, the early settlers in America began with only Indian and animal trails.

The first important highway in the New World was called the Boston Post Road.[7] It went between the cities of Boston and New York. In 1673 riders

[6] Although John McAdam was a Scotsman, most of his road building was done in England.

[7] Post roads were so-called because men or horses were posted, or placed, along them. Messages were passed from one rider to the next, so that there was no delay while a rider and his horse rested. Places where mail was handled were called *post offices*.

first began carrying mail over the Boston Post Road.

The first hard-surfaced road in the United States was finished in 1795.[8] To pay for the road, tolls were charged. There were nine tollgates along it. To travel on the road cost from one penny to 13½ ¢ a mile, depending on the size of the wagon and the number of horses. Today we have many toll roads in the United States.

[8] This stone road, called the Lancaster Turnpike, went from Philadelphia to Lancaster, Pennsylvania. It was the first important macadamized road in America.

As roads in the New World improved, bigger and bigger wagons traveled on them. A common means of travel was the huge Conestoga wagon.[9] It was drawn by six very large horses and carried freight as well as people. Sometimes 50 to 100 of these wagons traveled in a train.

The driver of the Conestoga wagon controlled his team by a whip and a single rein to the left leader horse. Since the Conestoga wagon has no seat for the driver, he often walked to the left of the last pair of horses.[10] This put his right hand, in which he carried the whip, nearer the horses. When two of these huge wagons met, the drivers of each kept to the middle of the road. This gave them a clear view of the road ahead, but it forced their horses to the right-hand side.

Because the Conestoga wagons took up so much room on the narrow roads of this period, and made

[9] The first Conestoga wagon was manufactured in the Conestoga Valley of Pennsylvania about 1725.

[10] Sometimes the driver of the Conestoga wagon rode the left wheel horse.

such deep wheel tracks, all other traffic was forced to move as they did. This brought about the American practice of moving on the right side of the road.[11]

From 1830–1900 there was not much change in road surfaces. Then with the invention of the automobile, better roads were needed. Again the vehicle creates the road. Since 1900, macadam roads have been improved.[12] Several other kinds of surfaces have also come into common use.[13]

In the United States alone, there are now over three million miles of roads!

It has been suggested that someday roads will not be needed because of the use of airplanes and new kinds of vehicles. No one knows for certain what the future will bring. Yet it seems likely that man will always travel on or near the surface of the land, whether it be on the earth or on other planets he may visit.

[11] The American practice of driving on the right is opposite from the practice in England and some other parts of the world. Yet, both of these customs probably developed from the same basic fact—that many people are right-handed.

[12] Stone, sand, gravel, and cement are mixed together. Tar is then applied to several layers of this mixture—one layer at a time. We sometimes call these roads "blacktop."

[13] Concrete and asphalt are popular materials.

PEBBLES IN THE PASSAGE

About 2,300 years ago the first attempt to conquer the world was made. From the kingdom of Macedonia, north of Greece, an army moved into Egypt, through the Persian Empire, and on to India. The leader of this army was a most remarkable man. His adventures will live forever in myth and legend.

Some legends contain elements of fact, while others are completely untrue. The main purpose of a legend is to glorify a hero. But sometimes a legend may also help us understand a great man.

Such a man was King Alexander.

"Onward! Onward!" The shout rang through the air. The tired, straggling army of soldiers and horses began to move. They had been traveling for several years. Many of the men were sick or had been hurt in the fighting. More wished for their homeland and the families they had left behind. Still Alexander, their king, led them ever onward.

Young King Alexander rode at the front of his straggling troops. He looked quite handsome dressed all in white and seated on a solid black horse. He turned to the man beside him.

"The men complain now, for they forget the delights of victory. Wait until their eyes feast on the precious stones of Asia!"

"And what if they do not live to enjoy those riches?" asked Hephaestion, Alexander's best friend. He could speak to the young king frankly.

Alexander shrugged his shoulders. "Then there will be more riches for the others," he said.

"And will you never be satisfied? We Greeks have already won most of the civilized world. When will we be done with victories?"

"Never!" Alexander straightened his shoulders and tossed his head. "I must go farther. Europe and Asia are not yet one empire. All people must be taught the fine Greek ways."

"By the gods, that is quite an undertaking!" Hephaestion stared at his friend.

"Yes, and it is by the gods that we shall do it! They will help us. Remember, it may well be true— as my mother has said—that I am actually the son of a god!"

"Perhaps . . ." Hephaestion muttered doubtfully, "perhaps."

The route led through an underground passageway. Hephaestion and Alexander entered first, followed by the soldiers on horseback. Though the way was dark, bright sparks began to flash about as the horses' hoofs struck the pebbles on the ground. Curious, some of the soldiers dismounted and began to collect a few of the pebbles. Others were too tired and remained on their horses. Then as the army began to move forward again, a voice resounded through the passageway.

"He who gathers some of these pebbles will be sorry. He who gathers none at all will be even sorrier."

The words were puzzling indeed. The men were still wondering about them when they came to the end of the passageway. Out in the bright sunlight they stopped to study the queer stones. It was then that they beheld not coarse pebbles—but diamonds and other precious gems!

A smile grew on the king's face as he watched his astonished soldiers. Yes, the gods were with him. Then his strong voice won the attention of the excited soldiers.

"The words you heard in the passage should be clear to you now," he shouted. "Those who gathered SOME pebbles are surely sorry that they did not gather more. Those who gathered NONE are even sorrier. The gods have given you a sign of the wonderful riches that lie ahead. Surely they are worth all the hardships!"

The soldiers were soon back on the march, renewed in spirit. Once more the clever king had lit the interest of his men.

Hephaestion turned to Alexander. "But you," he said, "collected no pebbles. On this journey what will you keep for yourself?"

"Hope," the king answered, smiling at his friend.

Hephaestion looked back at the battle-worn troop of men, who for the time were cheered by thoughts of precious gems. *Hope,* he thought, *is what drives all men on. In the days to come, Alexander will have need of hope.*

Yet Hephaestion, like other men of his time, couldn't help admiring the king for his ability to encourage his followers. Hephaestion would not be surprised to learn that one day King Alexander would be known as the famous Alexander the Great!

 When your **spirits** are raised you feel happier, livelier, and breathe more easily. Originally spirit meant "to breathe." What do we mean when we talk about a spirited horse?

Say What You Mean

In writing a story, an author must be careful to choose the right words. Often, several words will do, but only one will say exactly what the author wants said. Read the following:

Pat *looked* at the picture.

Does the word *looked* tell you very much about how Pat felt or acted?

Below are some different words that tell how Pat looked at the picture. Substitute each word for *looked* (you may have to drop *at* to make the sentence read correctly).

Tell how each substituted word changed your idea of Pat's action.

ex am ine (eg zam′ən), look at closely and carefully

gaze (gāz), look long and steadily

glance (glans), look quickly

ob serve (əb zėrv′), look at scientifically

peer (pēr), look closely to see clearly

squint (skwint), look with the eyes partly closed

stare (stãr), look long and directly with the eyes wide open

THEY BROUGHT MAPS TO LIFE

"Now you listen to me, young man," the captain of the small ship spoke sharply. "The island of Malekula is no place to go. I don't want to scare the little lady, but the people there are head-hunters. They still practice cannibalism!"

Martin Johnson smiled. He knew all that. Why, that was the very reason he and his wife, Osa, had come halfway around the world. "With plenty of tobacco and trade goods we should be safe enough," he replied.

"And anyway," Osa put in, "why should they hurt us? We only want to take their pictures."

"Take their pictures!" The captain laughed. "If you get close enough for that you'll be headed for their dinner table. I'm willing to take you to a nearby island, but I won't land on Malekula."

The year was 1917. Making motion pictures was a new art, and the Johnsons hoped to make a business of it. They knew that there were many places in the world that people in the United States knew little about. They wanted to visit these areas and film the country, people, and animals so that these dead spots on the map would come alive to the people back home. The island of Malekula was one of the few places left that had not been touched by civilization. Now that they were so near their goal, the captain didn't want to stop!

"You've been sailing the South Seas for years," Martin spoke again to the captain. "What do you know about these natives on Malekula?"

"Enough to know that I don't want to meet any of them. There are about 40,000 cannibals in two tribes. The smaller group is called the Small Numbers. The larger tribe is called the Big Numbers. The chief of the Big Numbers, Nagapate, could scare the dead!"

"And what do they do that's so frightening?" Martin wanted to know.

"Besides being cannibals, they bury their old people alive. They knock out the front teeth of their women when they marry, and the girls and women are never allowed to take a bath."

"Listen!" Osa interrupted. "What's that noise?"

"Oh, that," the captain said. "It's the natives beating their *boo-boos*. That's what they call their drums. They must be gathering for a feast."

Martin and Osa shuddered, yet they were more eager than ever to film these strange people. Martin was unable to change the captain's mind. A short time later the captain dropped them off at an island about a mile from Malekula. There Martin met a man who agreed to let him borrow a boat. The man also offered the help of five boys. After loading their cameras, film, and trade goods, the group set sail.

As the party neared the rocky shore of Malekula, they searched for signs of unfriendly natives. Not a person could be seen. Not even a breath of air stirred the yellow sand. Boldly they stepped out of the boat.

"How does this look to you?" Martin asked Osa.

"Fine, I guess, but where are all the cannibals?"

"Back in the bush, I suppose, plenty of them!"

"Looks like a trail over there," Osa pointed.

Just then a single native came out of the bush. The five boys moved back toward the boat. The sight of the man was very frightening indeed. Through his nose was a piece of human bone, and around his neck hung a string of pig's teeth. He was terribly dirty and he held his arms tightly as if he were in pain. He spoke, surprisingly, in a strange form of English.

"Master! Me belly walk about too much!"

Both Martin and Osa drew a deep breath and laughed loudly. They had expected to meet great danger, and instead they met only a native with a stomach ache! Osa reached into a bag and handed him some pills, which he swallowed all at once.

During this unexpected meeting, ten or more cannibals had slipped quietly out of the jungle. Each looked more terrible than the first, but seemed to be just as harmless. Hurriedly Martin set up his camera and began taking pictures. The natives kept talking all the time and pointing toward the jungle. Martin thought they meant that their chief was there and wanted them to come to him.

"You mean," Osa exclaimed, "the Big Numbers chief—Naga . . ."

"Sh!" warned Martin. "Don't say his name."

"But if only we could get him on the camera!" Osa cried excitedly.

"It would be worth the entire trip," agreed Martin.

With the boys leading the way, Martin and Osa plunged into the jungle. Scrambling and climbing through sharp brush and dense forest, they finally came to a clearing. They looked back, and far below they could see the yellow sand and their boat, a small dot on the water.

Hearing a noise, they turned back toward the clearing. Many natives carrying weapons had come up behind them.

"Don't let them see you're afraid," Martin whispered to Osa. "Leave the trade goods on the ground and start backing down the trail. I'll get them interested in the camera."

Osa started to leave, but the trail was cut off by more cannibals, perhaps a hundred or more. Then from the jungle came the beat of the *boo-boos*. All heads turned at once. Suddenly into the clearing burst the largest, fiercest, most frightening cannibal of all.

"Nagapate!" Martin and Osa whispered together.

"Remember to open the trade goods," Martin said quietly. "Show no fear—and smile."

"Hello, Mr. Nagapate," Osa began. She held out some tobacco. Nagapate reached out, but instead of taking the tobacco he grabbed her arm.

"He's just curious about your light skin," said Martin calmly, and continued grinding the camera.

Osa saw that the chief had rings on each finger. She wondered if they were souvenirs of his victories, and tried to keep from shaking. With her other hand she offered him the tobacco again. He took it and threw it to the ground.

"He won't take it, Martin, what shall I do?"

"Keep calm, dear, I'm going to try something."

Martin then left the camera and stepped between them. He took Nagapate's hand and shook it. The puzzled chief frowned. He had never seen this form of greeting.

Again Osa started to back away. Quickly Chief Nagapate turned, grabbed Osa's hand, and shook it.

She laughed and returned the shake. But Nagapate would not let go of her hand. She started to scream. Suddenly the chief set her free.

Nagapate grunted an order, and the cannibals returned to the jungle. The loud beat of the *boo-boos* stopped. What had happened! Osa didn't know, but she began to run down the trail. Martin grabbed the camera and followed. The five boys ran behind them.

Osa tripped and fell. As Martin helped her up, he looked toward the water. "A patrol boat!" he gasped. "They must think it's coming for us. If only it will stay until we reach our boat!"

They continued to run. The patrol boat was steaming away. The *boo-boos* began again, and the cannibals came running. Somehow the Johnsons reached their boat in time.

As they pushed away from the shore, Nagapate's men came running down the beach. Martin calmly continued taking a few more feet of film!

A few months later the civilized world shuddered at the sight of Nagapate's cruel face on the screen. Malekula was the first of many dead spots the Johnsons were to bring to life.

This first film was so successful that the next year the Johnsons returned to Nagapate's Island. This time they had with them three ships, sixty-five trunks, cases, and boxes, three white men, and twenty-six armed, friendly natives. They showed Nagapate the film they had made of him the year before. This time he seemed friendly. The Johnsons felt they had no more cause to fear the cannibals of this South Sea island.

 The Latin word *camera* meant "a room" or "a chamber." A picture-taking instrument is called a **camera** because it has a dark chamber where the picture is focused on the film.

GRANDFATHER'S ADVICE

This story has long been a favorite with fathers, and even more with grandfathers. It is one of the folk tales of the Lettish peasants who since time out of mind have been farming the land south of the Gulf of Riga.

When the world was young and new, people thought everything should be young and new. And so when a man got old, and could not do his share of work any longer, they had no use for him.

It was the custom to get rid of those old fellows who were only a burden.

Now there was a man who had an old father and a little son. The grandfather was very weak and scarcely moved from his place near the stove.

"The old man is useless," the man said to himself. "And he seems to have no idea of dying. I shall have to get rid of him."

So he took his little son's sled and piled the old grandfather onto it.

"What are you doing with Grandfather?" asked the little boy.

"I am putting him on your sled. Have you no eyes?" said the man grumpily.

"But where are you taking him?" asked the little boy.

"To the forest," said the man.

"Whatever for?" asked the little boy.

"Never mind," said the man. Even though it was such a sensible thing to do, he did not quite like the idea of getting rid of the old grandfather.

"Let me come along!" begged the little boy.

"Be off with you!" said his father. "And stop bothering me with your foolish questions."

"Please let me come along," begged the little boy. "Please! I won't ask another question. But please let me come!"

"Come if you must," said the man angrily.

So the little boy hopped along after the sled, taking many short steps to the man's big ones, and careful not to ask another question.

Finally they came to the forest. The man dropped the rope with which he had been pulling the sled, shrugged his shoulders, shook his head, and turned around to go home. It seemed a hard thing to leave the old grandfather there in the forest to die, but that was the custom. And who is brave enough to go against custom?

But his little son tugged at his coat.

"You mustn't leave Grandfather here in the forest," he said in a small voice. "He will surely die."

"He is too old to work," said the man. "It is the only sensible thing to do." And he began marching homeward. The little boy ran after him, and pulled at his coat.

"What's the matter now?" the man asked grumpily.

"Daddy," said the little boy. "You mustn't leave my sled there!"

"And why not?" asked the man.

"Because when you are old and worn out, I'll need the sled to carry you to the forest!"

"Perhaps," the man said to himself, "I haven't done such a sensible thing after all. When I get old, my son will do with me as I have done with his grandfather."

This displeased him quite as much as the idea of leaving the old grandfather in the forest. So he turned to his son and said, "You are right, and I was wrong. We'll go and fetch Grandfather home again."

So he went back to fetch the sled and the grandfather. But he did not let the neighbors know that he had brought the old man home again. After all, he was going against custom, and that is a risky thing to do. So he hid the old grandfather away in the cellar, and took him food and drink in secret.

Now it happened that not long afterward there was a famine in the land. There were seven years of bad harvest. Certainly nobody was going to be bothered feeding the old fellows. Nobody but this one man. He kept on taking food to the old grandfather in his hiding place. But he took smaller and smaller portions. The old grandfather noticed this, but he said nothing.

The famine was a terrible one. People ate up every bit of food they could get. They ate their wheat down to the very last grain and they ate their rye down to the very last grain. When it was time for sowing, there was not even seed grain left. Nobody knew what to do next. If they had not got rid of the old men, they might have asked advice from them. But the wisdom of the old had died with them.

One day the man who had kept his old father hidden took him his dinner with a sorry face. The dinner was nothing but a piece of bread. And it was a very small piece. It was not fine wheaten bread. It was not even tasty rye bread. It was coarse bread made of barley flour.

"Ah," sighed the old grandfather. "I am very hungry. But I don't know that I can eat this barley bread. I have the stomach for it right enough. But I haven't the teeth for it. I don't ask for fine wheaten bread. But a piece of rye bread now, that would be tasty! Even a very little piece."

"There is famine," said the man. "There is no rye flour to make bread with. There is not even a grain of rye left for sowing."

"Well," said the old grandfather. "That's bad, but it could be worse. You still have a roof of thatch on your threshing barn I suppose. Take the old straw off half the roof and thresh it well. You'll find quite a little grain has been left in the thatch."

The man did as the old grandfather advised. He took half the thatch off the roof, threshed the straw, and got a whole jugful of grain. Then he went to tell the old grandfather about it.

"That's good, but it could be better," said the old grandfather. "Put back the threshed thatch, take the other half off the roof, thresh that, and you will get another jugful of grain."

The man did as the old grandfather advised. It happened just as he had said it would. Then he went to the old grandfather and told him about it.

"Good," said the grandfather. "Plant your grain. Perhaps you will get a crop."

And so the man did, and in good time he got a fine crop of rye.

When the neighbors discovered his good fortune, they came crowding around to ask him how he had come by his seed grain.

"I got good advice from my old father," said the man.

"How could that be?" they asked. "You have no father!"

"Oh, but I have!" he answered. And he brought the old man out of hiding.

"That's my grandfather!" said the boy proudly.

After that nobody thought of getting rid of the old men. They were respected for their wisdom, which the old keep just as the thatch keeps the seeds.

At one time the nickname for Joan, a common name among servants, was "Jug." The word **jug** came to mean any woman, especially a woman servant. Later it referred to the object she often carried.

THE END OF THE ROAD

My name is Joe Frost. I drive a cab in Boston, but right now I'm on vacation. This year I wanted to escape from the city noises and traffic jams, so I went west to visit the old ghost towns. I arrived in Gold Gulch yesterday.

Gold Gulch was once a lively town, but everybody left when the mine petered out and the stream dried up. There's still good hunting, though, in the hills around here.

I set out early this morning and managed to get a bird with the first shot. It landed at the base of a hill. When I stooped down I noticed that the bird was lying on a newspaper. I picked it up along with the bird and took them both back to my cabin. It was just a few minutes ago that I took time to look at the paper.

It looked new—as if it had just come off the press. The name of it was THE EVENING SUN, and the date was May 15, 2050. 2050! I thought it was a joke until I read the story at the bottom of the page. Now I'm not so sure.

Some of the words were strange to me, so I'm going to tell you the story in my own words.

The sun was shining brightly and the air was quite warm. Page Young felt restless, so he decided to explore the countryside in his *GEM* (Ground Effect Machine). He climbed in the machine, turned on the engine, and started the lift fan. The GEM rose easily into the air and floated about a foot off the ground. He set the air-blast handle to "Forward" and drifted into the main traffic lane and out of the town.

For a while Page followed the old toll road. Of course, no one collected tolls any more. Since there were no wheeled vehicles, the roads didn't need to be kept in good shape. A GEM rode on cushions of air instead of on wheels. It could travel over ice, snow, sand, water, fields—almost any surface that had no bumps over six inches high. However, traffic still had to be controlled. That's why most traffic lanes followed the old roads or railroad tracks.

Page rode slowly along enjoying the breeze that blew through the open window. Then a sign up ahead caught his attention. It said:

That meant there must be a path in the woods on which bicycles and wagons could be used. He kept his eyes open for the cutoff.

SMALL WHEELED VEHICLES PERMITTED HERE

In order to keep the aircars from trespassing on other people's land, rocks were placed along the lanes. Where a break in the rocks appeared, a GEM could leave the main lane of traffic.

As he neared the path, Page moved the handle that changed the direction of the air blasts and his GEM moved sideways out of the traffic and between the rocks. Another change, and he moved forward up the path.

No one else seemed to be enjoying this part of the woods today. Page turned to look back at the stream of traffic he had left. As he did so, his arm hit the air-blast handle. The aircar swung off the path, narrowly missing several trees. It was headed straight for a nearby hill. The GEM scraped a large rock. Page managed to cut off the powerful lift fan, and the aircar settled smoothly to the ground just inches from the hill. Shaking a bit, Page opened the door and climbed out to study the damage.

It was as he had feared. The GEM wouldn't go any place without repairs. He was gazing into space trying to decide what to do when he caught sight of what appeared to be a tunnel, or a passage, through the hill. He walked over to investigate.

The tunnel was fairly wide, but not too long or dark. Page hesitated a moment and then decided to see where it came out.

When he was halfway through the tunnel, voices reached his ears. He paused to listen, but

it was hard to make out any words. Hoping that he might find help, he continued on his way.

As he came into the daylight again, he stared in amazement. A lovely valley lay ahead. It looked like a picture in a history book. To the left were a few buildings made of logs. A dirt road ran past them and out into the hills beyond. To his right a winding stream cut through a cliff. Strangely dressed men lined the bank of the stream. Most of them were stooping over and moving something in the water. As they did so, they shouted back and forth. Page managed to catch a few words such as "strike," "pan," "gold," and "beans." He couldn't imagine what they were talking about, but at least they were people. There was no one else to help him. Slowly Page made his way toward the stream.

The man nearest him was working quite apart from the others. Page approached him. "How do you do? Could you please tell me the name of this place?"

The man stood up and wiped a hand across his forehead. His eyes grew wide as he looked at Page's clothes. "You really ARE a stranger in these parts. This town's called Gold Gulch. Where are you from?"

"My car was disabled on the other side of that tunnel." Page pointed in the direction from which he had come.

"Tunnel? Funny, I never noticed that before. Didn't know the coach ever came from that way." He looked up at the sun. "The next one isn't due for several hours."

Page wasn't sure what the man was talking about, but he decided to find out more about this place. Down the stream the others were still going through their strange performance. "Tell me", he said, "what's everybody doing?"

"Doing!" the man exclaimed. "Why, sonny, haven't you ever panned for gold?"

"Panned for gold?" Page repeated. "No, sir, but I've read about it. I didn't think there was any left to pan."

"Well, now," the man looked surprised, "there's still enough for those who will work for it. Of course, some of the land's a bit worked out since the gold rush of '49."

"Goodness, I didn't hear about any gold rush last year." Page was really becoming puzzled.

"Not last year," the man said grumpily. "In '49—that was ten years ago. Where have you been?"

"Oh, around." Suddenly a crazy idea began to form in Page's mind. He decided to make a guess. "This is 1859 isn't it?" he ventured.

The man gave Page a puzzled look and began to back away. "I can't stand here talking all day. There's work to do."

Page watched the man as he dipped into the sand of the stream bed. Finally the man said, "Fetch me the pan on the ledge over there. If you're going to wait for the next coach, you might as well help. Maybe you'll have a stroke of luck."

Page did as he was told, but his mind was else-where. *If somehow I've passed through a hole in time and gone back 200 years, these men aren't going to be much help with a GEM.*

Still he might learn *something* from them, and he was eager to see this coach the man talked about. Page watched closely as the man began to work, and then followed his movements.

With the pans the two men dug up stones, water, and sand from the stream bed. It was a muddy mess. Then they held their pans about an inch under the water and moved them back and forth. As the stones turned over, they pushed them out

with their thumbs. They kept this up for about half an hour, though it seemed longer to Page. He wasn't used to all the stooping over.

Finally only about a spoonful of black sand remained in the pans. The man spread a large handkerchief on the ground, and carefully poured the contents of his pan on the handkerchief. Page followed suit. The water seeped through the handkerchiefs leaving the "sand" to dry in the sun.

The hot sun did its work quickly. Soon the man brought out a magnet and a small jar. He moved the magnet lightly over the surface of the sand. Small bits of black iron stuck to the magnet, leaving specks of gold on the handkerchief. Then he carefully put the shining flakes in the jar. He offered to do this for Page, and then gave him the jar with its glistening flakes of gold.

Suddenly a roaring and grinding noise filled the air. A shout went up and everyone began to race toward the road, as four horses appeared pulling what seemed to Page to be a large box on wheels. "The Stage! The Stage!" resounded through the hills.

"There's your ride," the man nodded to Page, and they joined the running crowd.

The man, with his longer legs, reached the stage first. Page watched curiously while people and boxes were being unloaded. He saw the man speak to the driver and then point his way. Page moved closer. The man motioned to him, and Page walked over to the two men.

"The driver says he's never seen that·tunnel before, either," the man said, "but if you'll give

him your gold dust he'll take you through to the next town."

Page handed the driver his jar. He wished he didn't have to part with it. It would have made a fine souvenir. Still, he had to get home somehow and a stagecoach ride would be something to talk about—if anyone would believe him.

Page climbed in and shut the door. As the coach began to move he turned to look out the window. The man was grinning and waving. Page waved, too, and then was thrown back into his seat as the coach picked up speed.

It wasn't long before they reached the tunnel. The horses slowed their pace as they made their way through it. A few feet on the other side the coach came to a stop, and the horses began to whinny loudly as if in great fear. They would go no farther.

Page could do nothing but climb out of the coach. At least it had taken him back to the year 2050. Now he saw that the sun was setting and the woods were beginning to grow dark. He raced toward the old toll road, noticing as he ran that his GEM was still where he had left it. He stopped once to look back, but the stagecoach was nowhere to be seen.

Page reached the traffic lane and began to run alongside of it. It wasn't long before a GEM patrol car left the lane and settled to the ground just ahead of him. Patrol cars were larger than passenger vehicles, and they rode higher off the ground. Therefore, they could pass over the rocks that marked the lanes.

Page climbed in, gave the patrolman his address, and muttered something about a breakdown. He said his father would take care of it and explained no more. Soon they reached the house. Page called a "thank you, sir," and dashed in.

That night as Page drifted off to sleep, he began to wonder if the whole thing had really happened. Some of the events seemed a little foggy now. His parents hadn't believed his story, but he had expected that. Well, the morning would tell the tale. His father had promised to go back to the spot with him.

The next morning Page and his father followed the same route the boy had taken the day before. They found the disabled GEM easily enough. The damage wasn't too great, and Mr. Young quickly repaired it. But the tunnel? Page wandered up

and down the hillside, but nowhere could he find
an opening of any sort. He was about to give up,
when he caught sight of something. "Come here,
Dad, look at these marks on the ground."

Mr. Young walked over to where Page stood.
There, coming straight out of a solid wall, were
the tracks of a heavy, wheeled vehicle. They
stretched only a few feet into the woods and then
stopped. They did not turn around and go back—
they just stopped. It was as if the vehicle that had

made them, like the GEM's of the year 2050, had literally come to the end of the road.

For a moment Mr. Young stared silently at the tracks. He couldn't begin to explain them. But he knew that for Page, at least, there could be no punishment.

Well, that's the gist of my story. But I wonder how that newspaper got there? Did the hole in time open up again? If so, will the tunnel appear yet a third time? I'd like to visit the world of 2050—a GEM might be a lot better than my cab. I'm going to look for that tunnel. That's why I'm writing all this down. If I don't come back, you'll know where I am and won't worry. If I'm lucky, this won't be the end of the road for me, but the beginning of an adventure.

 A person giving a **performance** on the stage wants to do the best or most finished acting he can do. *Perform* comes from two French words meaning "to finish through."

Making Sentences More Meaningful

Not long ago we learned that it was possible to substitute different words for *looked* in the sentence *Pat looked at the picture.* The words we used were just a few of the verbs we could have used, such as *frowned* and *smiled*.

Now we will study another way to make the action clearer to the reader. Let's use the sentence *Amelia read the directions.* Instead of substituting a word for the verb *read*, we are going to add words to modify, or further explain, it.

First, try the word *seriously*. Where would you put this word in the sentence? How does the added word make Amelia's action clearer to you? Add the following words or groups of words to the sentence about Amelia. Explain how she read the directions.

curiously	hesitatingly	steadily
fearfully	in bewilderment	laughingly
miserably	in amazement	in wonder
happily	in a loud voice	quietly
naturally	yesterday	doubtfully

Think of other words or groups of words that can be used to modify *read*.

THE PROUD TRAIN

Characters

Reporter, a little bored with his assignment to interview
    a train

Conductor, whose "All Aboard!" sounds like a song

Chorus, which, as "The Train," is very sure and proud
    of itself

Solos, spoken loudly and clearly in different pitches

Reporter: I'm supposed to get a story. Let's see . . . Who are you?

All Chorus: I am a train.

Reporter: Hmmmm, everybody knows what a train looks like.

Chorus I: Like a big long silvery snake sliding up the track—

Chorus II: With the torn black-feather smoke pouring out the stack.

Reporter: What else?

Chorus I: With a thousand windows to give back the light—

Chorus II: And a thousand wheels to rush through the night—and carry me fast and far.

All Chorus: THAT'S what I look like.

Reporter: Is that all?

All Chorus: That's enough!

Chorus I: When I stop for a minute on the station tracks,

And the crowds come pouring through my open doors—

Chorus II: And they wave good-by, and they settle on the seats,

And the conductor calls—

Conductor: All Aboard! All Aboard!

Reporter: Well?

All Chorus: That's enough!

Chorus I: Or do you want to know what makes me go?

The red that says stop or the light that says slow?

Chorus II: The signals and the lights and the telegraph key

All working at once for me—

Chorus I:	Me—
All Chorus:	ME!
Reporter:	You think a lot of yourself.
Chorus I:	I take the bankers to crowded New York.
Chorus II:	I bring back cattle from the western plains, Through thunder and lightning and snows and rains.
Chorus I:	Coal and iron and lumber and wheat! Without my carrying there'd be—
Reporter:	(*Interrupts*) I know—nothing to eat. Haven't you forgotten?
All Chorus:	What?
Reporter:	Buses.
All Chorus:	Bah!
Reporter:	Automobiles.
All Chorus:	Bah!
Reporter:	Trucks.
All Chorus:	Bah!
Reporter:	Boats.

All Chorus:	Steamboats, tugboats, riverboats, sailboats—Bah! bah! bah! bah! bah!—And again, bah!
Reporter:	You sound like a billy goat.
Chorus I:	I'm the most beautiful thing there is, And the fastest for its size.
Chorus II:	When they hand out medals, I walk off with every prize.
Reporter:	What about people? You must have carried a lot of people in your time. Whom did you like best?
All Chorus:	Best? There is no best. They're all the same, If you don't know their name.
Solo I:	Women with hats,
Solo II:	And boys with bats,
Solo III:	And men with books,
Solo IV:	And cops and cooks,
Solo V:	And soldiers and sailors,
Solo VI:	And drivers of trailers!

Solo VII: And some are sad,

Solo VIII: And some are glad.

All Chorus: There IS no best!

Reporter: At last you've said something I can agree with.

All Chorus: I've seen a lot and I've done still more; I've rolled every run from shore to shore.

Chorus I: My boilers are patched and I've been refitted,

Chorus II: But my speed's still there when I'm permitted!

All Chorus: The planes may come and the planes may go, They'll never get rid of me here below! And I've got friends just like myself; We'll never, never be put on the shelf. You've heard them talk about the stars? (*Whispers*) I'll tell you a secret— I'm going to MARS!

Reporter: Now, wait a minute!

All Chorus: You don't have to believe—just wait and see. They'll launch me with rockets—yes, me, just me.

Chorus I: They're making their plans, they've
      marked my sides
      Where the rivets go for the rocket
      slides.

Chorus II: They knew what they were doing when
      they picked this train,
      Around whose stack hung the golden
      chain.
      (*Talks as if presenting a medal*)
      "Most powerful stroke, most passenger
      miles,
      Outstanding performance in railroad
      trials."

Conductor: All Aboard! 'Board!

Reporter: Look, friend, I hate to break up your dreams, but the conductor's calling.

All Chorus: I heard him.

Reporter: You'd better go then.

All Chorus: Don't hurry me. I must wait for the signal—

Conductor: 'Board!

All Chorus: And there it is!

I'm off! Good-by!

Reporter: Good-by.

All Chorus: (*Gains speed as wheels move*)

I'm off, off-off-off,

Off, off-off-off,

Off-off-off-off,

Off-off-off-off,

Whooo—Whoooo—

Good-by-----!

At one time a man's wealth was measured by the number of **cattle** he owned. *Cattle* comes from the Latin word *caput* meaning "head." Today we still talk about a herd of a hundred head.

Unit Five

Workers and Weavers

Word Meaning from Sentences

The dictionary defines words. Many times it uses the words in sentences or in phrases to help you understand their meanings.

bal let (bal′ ā), a type of dance by a group on the stage: *Dancers leaped and twirled in the beautiful ballet.*

de clare (di klãr′), say strongly: *"The sun is certainly hot today," she declared.*

drain (drān), flow off slowly: *The water will drain out of the sink.*

en dure (en dür′), stand; bear: *I can't endure the cold weather.*

glow (glō), a warm feeling: *He felt a glow of pride when he won the prize.*

grad u al (graj′ ü əl), little by little; slow: *There was a gradual rise in the temperature.*

groan (grōn), a short, deep moan: *A groan from the boys was heard when the second bus failed to stop.*

seize (sēz), grab suddenly: *The little dog seized the bone.*

skill (skil), ability developed through practice: *Playing the organ takes skill.*

THE BIGGEST NOBODY

Katie leaned against the school wall. It was hard, getting to be one of a bunch when you're a newcomer in a small town. Oh, the girls were all friendly enough, but they had known each other since first grade. They had memories and jokes together from way back, and Katie John was still an outsider.

Thank the luck she had Sue for a best friend! But she did wish someone else would notice her sometimes, too. And Sue was out of school today with a cold. "I'm the biggest Nobody in my whole class," she muttered. She felt so cold and alone and sad that she could almost cry.

The bell rang and Katie went into the school building with the other children.

The morning passed as usual until just before recess, when their teacher made an announcement. The P.T.A. needed the children's help to sell tickets to a ballet. As a reward, the class that sold the most tickets would be given a movie projector. Actually, the movie projector would belong to the whole school system, but when not in use, it would stay with the class that sold the most tickets.

Katie John was excited at the thought of seeing a ballet troupe dance. Oh, her folks just had to take her to the ballet!

At recess, everyone was talking about the contest.

"Probably the sixth grade will win. They think they're so big at everything."

"Or else some room at North Side School. North Side always wins stuff."

"My mother says if I bring home anything more to sell she'll disown me," one boy said.

One of the pretty girls shrugged her shoulders delicately, saying, "I'd be afraid to go knocking on doors, asking strangers to buy tickets."

"Well, I wouldn't," Katie John spoke up. "I sold lots of tickets to school things back in California. All you have to do is believe people are going to want whatever you're selling. When you go up to a door you think, *This is Mrs. Wood's chance in a lifetime to see a ballet.* And make her believe it, too."

Katie saw she had the attention of a number of her classmates. They'd paused around her before running out onto the playground. She felt a sudden glow at being the center of things.

"Yes, but what if people say 'no,' anyway?" she was asked.

"They won't," Katie bragged. "You kids sell what you can, and don't worry, I'll do the rest."

Katie John had not told the exact truth. People had said "no" sometimes when she was selling tickets back home, but she HAD been unusually successful. Certainly, here was her chance to be Somebody in her classroom.

Katie John took fifty tickets to sell. After school she raced home.

"Promise you'll buy three tickets for us to go?" she asked her mother breathlessly.

Katie John hurried out and started selling tickets before any of the other school children began working her neighborhood.

As she walked along, Katie John practiced her sales talk. She would *not* say, "You wouldn't want to buy a ticket, would you?" That was the way beginners did it. No, she would say, "How do you do? I'm Katie John Tucker. Have you ever gone to a ballet?" If the person said, "No," she'd say, "Then now's your chance." If the person said "Yes," she'd say, "Then you know how much fun it is." Then she'd tell about the ballet.

Even though Katie John had bragged about her ability to sell tickets, her hands were clammy. So much depended on her. She rang the first doorbell. A young woman came to the door.

"How do you do? I'm Katie John Tucker. Have you ever been to a ballet?"

"Look, Miss, are you selling something?" the woman asked, looking over her shoulder as a baby cried inside. "Because if you are, I don't want any." And the woman closed the door.

Katie went down the porch steps silently. Oh, well, every house wouldn't have crying babies.

Then up and down the street Katie John heard the same story. People didn't care about ballet dancers, or they couldn't afford tickets.

By dark she had sold only three tickets. Katie could feel the tears prickling close to falling. There was something awful about being turned down at door after door. She felt more Nobody than ever. And the kids at school were depending on her. What a fool she'd look after her bragging.

At home, Mother and Dad bought three tickets and one of their friends very nicely took two.

The next day on the way to school Katie wondered how she could face the children when they asked her how many tickets she'd sold. All she could do was try to look gay and mysterious.

Early in the afternoon the first snowfall of the year began. Katie John watched the snowflakes drift against the windows. By the time school was out, the snow had stopped, leaving a light covering on the ground.

I just have to sell tickets today, Katie thought, *even if I have to beg people. If only I could give them a bonus with each ticket.* But she didn't have anything to give away.

She wished she had time to play in the snow, but Dad said more was expected tonight. Maybe it would still be on the ground Saturday. Maybe there'd be big drifts and Dad would let her shovel the walks, and . . .

Shovel the walks. Hmmm. There was an idea! She could offer to shovel walks free for every person who bought ballet tickets! Now she had a bonus offer! People would be sure to buy.

And Katie was right. By dark she'd sold twenty-seven tickets and promised to shovel the walks at nine houses. Then she began to wonder how she'd get nine walks shoveled before suppertime tomorrow. Oh, well, there wasn't much snow. She ran home, jingling her pockets full of money.

At home she learned that the delivery boy had bought two tickets, so with the eight she'd sold yesterday, that made thirty-seven.

The next day the children were talking about how many tickets they'd sold—five, only three, seven. Katie waited until someone asked, "How many did you sell, Katie John?"

Calmly she said, "Oh, thirty-seven."

"Thirty-seven! Wow!"

Some of the boys patted her on the back and called her "good girl!" One girl sighed that she didn't see how Katie John could do it. Katie didn't tell her how, either.

Later Katie was overjoyed when their teacher announced that the count was in from the other schools, and their room had won the movie projector.

The girls shrieked and the boys yelled "Hurray!" "Good Old Katie!" someone yelled. Katie John was all a-prickle inside with delight. Now she wasn't a Nobody. She was "Good Old Katie." Happily she stared out at the snowy playground.

Gradually she began to notice what she was looking at. Snow. Great piles of snow. It lay in heavy drifts on the ground.

Oh, great goodness. Those nine snowy walks weren't going to be easy to shovel this afternoon. At recess Katie John secretly told Sue how she'd managed to sell so many tickets, and Sue promised to help her shovel snow.

After school they started at the house of the lady who had bought the first tickets. Her house was close to the street, and the walk to her porch wasn't long. Katie John had never shoveled snow before, but by watching Sue she soon learned to scoop and toss, scoop and toss.

"There! That's one finished!" Katie said breathlessly. But the lady tapped on a front window, and then appeared at the door.

"You haven't done the sidewalk," she called.

Katie John's heart sank. She hadn't realized that people had to keep the sidewalk in front of their houses clean. She had been thinking of the short front walks that ran from the houses to the street.

"Oh, glory!" she groaned. "We have the sidewalks to clean in front of eight more houses. That'll take forever. We'll never get done."

With determination the girls set to work again. Scoop and toss, scoop and toss. Their shoulders were beginning to ache and Katie could feel a blister starting on her hand.

Finally their first job was finished and they hurried on to the next. There the girls had a pleasant surprise. The man of the house had already done his walk. The next place was a fairly easy one, too. The house sat close to the street on a narrow lot so there was little to be done. Katie and Sue began scooping and tossing. All the fun had gone out of the work, but they soon had the walk cleared.

Six more to go! Katie straightened her aching back and groaned as she looked at the next house with its wide, beautiful lot.

"Hey, you girls. Getting paid for that?"

Katie and Sue lifted sore necks and saw three boys from their room: Howard, Sammy, and Pete. Katie shook her head in answer and wished they'd go on. But the boys hung around to watch the girls' shovels work.

"Did you ever see anybody work so slow?" Pete teased. "Why I could shovel faster than that and eat an apple at the same time."

Howard said, "I could shovel faster than that and read a comic book."

Sammy said, "I could shovel faster than that and —and—"

Katie John stopped and stared down at her shovel, wanting to throw it at them. Suddenly she looked up with a sparkle in her eye.

"Maybe Sammy could do it faster, but Howard and Pete couldn't," she declared.

"What do you mean?" Howard was a little angry. "I'm the biggest."

"But Sammy looks stronger," Katie said. "I bet he could do this whole big piece of sidewalk before you could do that little part over there."

"Give me that shovel." Howard grabbed it from Katie. "All right, we'll just see!"

303

Sammy seized Sue's shovel and the boys tore away at the snow. Katie looked at Sue trying to keep her face straight.

In a few minutes Howard had finished his piece. Sammy hadn't cleared all of his part, but he'd done so much that it looked as though he'd actually done more than Howard.

"Maybe Sammy couldn't do it all," Katie said to keep things going, "but he still worked faster than you did, Howard."

"He did not!" Howard said angrily.

"The only way you can really prove it is to time your work," said Sue, doing her part.

"Oh, they're all tired out now," Katie John smiled in a particularly maddening way.

"Maybe Sammy is, but I'm not," Howard yelled.

"All right then," said Katie. "Each of you do part of the sidewalk down at this house and we'll time you." It was her next shoveling job.

"Me, too," Pete said eagerly. "I can do better than either of them."

Shovels scraped, boys grunted, and the snow flew. Sue timed five-minute contests. By the time they'd cleared the walks at that place and the one next door Sue declared Howard the winner.

"Okay you were right," Katie John told the boys. "You can shovel faster than we can. Anyway, thanks a lot for the help." To Sue she added, "You'd better go home now. I'm rested and I only have three more places to do."

"Three more places?" Pete shouted. "Are you getting paid?"

"If you are, we should get a cut for helping!" Howard added.

"Why, you ungrateful things!" Sue exclaimed. "She's not getting paid. She's doing it for you."

Katie tried to quiet her. She didn't want the story going around school about how she'd sold all those tickets after her big talk about her successful sales system. But Sue went right on telling how Katie John had brought all this work on herself just to help their room win glory and the movie projector.

The boys hung their heads. Finally Pete looked straight at Katie. "You're a good sport, Katie John Tucker."

"You're all right," Sammy said.

"Hey, look, it's almost dark!" Howard talked fast. "You won't get done in time. We'll help you."

The boys ran home to get shovels. Soon everyone was shoveling harder than ever.

Katie's back ached, her shoulders ached, the backs of her legs were stripes of pain, and she had three, broken blisters on her hands. But she felt wonderful! Today she'd been called "Good Old Katie" and now "Good Sport." What more could a Nobody ask?

The sky was completely black and the street lights were on before Katie and the boys finished. Still she was able to eat supper and get to the ballet with her parents on time.

When the house lights dimmed, Katie John leaned back in the dark. She breathed deeply and slowly as she watched the colorful dancers through a happy haze. She was so tired it was like watching a ballet in a dream. *Possibly the nicest way of all to watch a ballet troupe dance*, she thought contentedly.

 Some words have entered the English language unchanged. The exact meaning of the Latin word *bonus* is "good," and everyone knows that a **bonus** is something good.

The Crow and the Jug

A crow was so thirsty, his throat was so raw

That he found it quite difficult even to caw.

He flew around looking for something to drink.

"Some swallows of water would help me, I think.

        It seems very plain

        We do need some rain.

        Without water I'm sure

        That I cannot endure

This very uncomfortable temperature."

Now just as it seemed he would die from the heat,
He chanced on a water jug down by the street
Where the market was held. Feeling lucky indeed
He lit on the edge. "This is just what I need!"
      He stuck in his beak
      Then let out a shriek
      And loudly complained
      The jug had been drained
Of most of the water that it had contained.

He wiggled and pushed but he just couldn't get
A droplet of water to make his bill wet.
He thought he might pull the jug down on its side
But this device failed as all others he tried.
      His hopes for a drink
      Were ready to sink
      When he suddenly eyed
      Some pebbles beside
The highway. "Now there's an idea!" he cried.

Even though he was feeling decidedly weak,
He managed to pick up a stone with his beak
And drop it right down in the jug. One by one
He added some more and the job was soon done.
> The water rose high.
> He no longer was dry
> For he reached with his bill
> And drank up his fill
Feeling quite proud of his inventive skill.

To this fable's lesson please give your attention.
Necessity's the mother of every invention.

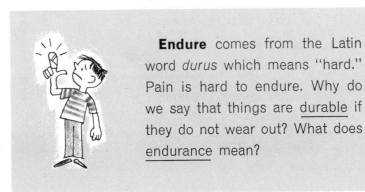

Endure comes from the Latin word *durus* which means "hard." Pain is hard to endure. Why do we say that things are durable if they do not wear out? What does endurance mean?

Word Meaning from Pictures

The pictures in a dictionary help you understand the meaning of words.

co co nut (kō′kə nut′), a large, round, hard-shelled fruit of the coco palm

coconut

fur nace (fėr′nis), a closed metal box in which a very hot fire is made

furnace

hem i sphere (hem′ə sfēr), half of a sphere or globe. *North America and South America are in the Western Hemisphere.*

hemisphere

ket tle (ket′əl), a metal container for boiling liquids, cooking foods, etc.

kettle

ol ive (ol′iv), the fruit of an evergreen tree that grows in warm countries

olive

vol ca no (vol kā′nō), an opening in the earth through which steam, ashes, and lava pour forth forming a hill

volcano

AN AMERICAN INVENTOR:
BILL STOUT

Young Bill Stout moaned as he turned off the alarm clock. He checked the time just to be sure. It was four o'clock in the morning. He lay in bed shivering for a moment. *Must be thirty below today,* he thought. *Wish someone else would turn on the heat.* Then, gathering his courage, he threw back the covers, grabbed his bathrobe, and tore down three flights of stairs to the cellar.

In the center of the cellar floor was a large furnace. Quickly he dropped the damper at the back and raised the draft in front. Once done, he raced up the stairs two at a time and jumped under the covers. By six o'clock, he knew, the heat would come up, the steam would be on, and the house warm. Day in and day out his mornings began in exactly the same way.

At this time Bill was going to school in Minnesota. He was living on the top floor of a private home. Instead of paying rent he had agreed to tend the furnace for the landlady, but the job

was not a pleasant one. At four in the morning the cold floor was hard on the feet and the early rising wasn't easy. It was even harder if he had studied late the night before. Besides, on cold mornings he complained that he was just plain lazy.

One morning when Bill had climbed back into bed, after his dash to the cellar, he thought about his furnace-tending problem. Perhaps there was a way to make his job easier. He knew that the damper and draft controlled the air flow through the furnace.

At night the draft was to be closed and the damper opened. This made the fire burn slowly, because very little air could flow through the furnace.

In the morning the draft was to be opened and the damper closed. Then the air could flow freely and the fire would burn brightly.

In homes of that time someone had to make these changes by hand. Suddenly Bill had a bright idea. Suppose he tied strings to the damper and draft. He could run them through the cellar window, outside the house, and up through his bedroom window. When the alarm clock went off he would have a very easy job.

In the morning he could get up, loosen one string which would drop the damper, and pull another string which would raise the draft. He wouldn't even have to go near the cellar! Later, when the house was warm, he could go down, lower the draft a little so the furnace and house wouldn't get too hot, and add more coal.

For a few weeks this method of furnace tending worked fine. Then one morning one of the strings broke and Bill was forced to make the full trip downstairs. The rest of the day he thought about the problem. Soon he had a new idea.

Bill took his alarm clock down to the cellar, fastened it to a board, and set it on the floor at the front of the furnace near the draft.

Then over the flat top of the furnace he put a crossbar in the shape of an upright T. One end of it extended over the damper and the other end extended over the draft. He placed the crossbar a little off balance. In its normal position, the end over the damper would be down, and the end over the draft would be up.

From the lowered end of the crossbar he fastened a wire to the damper while it was in its closed position. From the raised end of the crossbar he tied a wire to the draft while it was in its open position.

Next he tied a string to the end of the crossbar over the draft. He tested it just to be sure. When he pulled on the string, the draft closed and the damper opened. When he let go, the parts returned to their normal position.

Of course he didn't want to work the string by hand. So he fastened a short stick to the end of the string. Then he placed the stick under the winding key of the alarm clock.

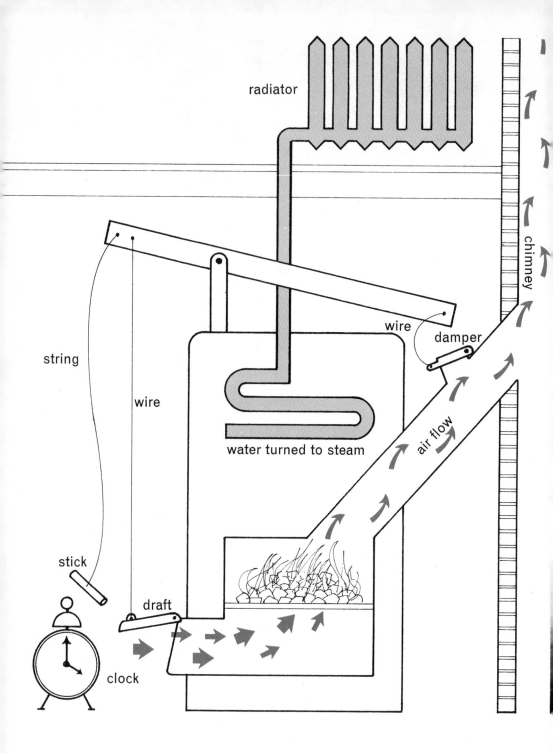

Automatic Furnace Tender in Normal Position

At night he could set the alarm. When it went off, the winding key would turn and loosen the stick. The crossbar would be freed and would return to its normal position. This action would open the draft and close the damper.

On the first morning that Bill tried his new invention, quite a disturbance was created. The night before he had set the clock for 4 A.M. Then he had carefully placed the stick under the winding key and gone upstairs prepared for a good night's sleep. Suddenly, in the early morning hours, the whole household was startled out of its sleep by a loud ringing. Bill had forgotten to take the alarm bell off the clock! After he took care of this, he and the whole household could sleep peacefully in the mornings. This invention he called his Automatic Furnace Tender.

At the time, Bill was writing stories for a Minnesota newspaper. Every week he told about some new device he had created, and drew a picture of it. Bill had always enjoyed developing mechanical toys and it was usually these he wrote about. Now the furnace idea sounded like a good one. He sent in the story and received five dollars for it.

Three months later a new company was formed in Minnesota. It made a heat regulator which was an alarm clock device for the furnace. Later developments improved this device and it became known as a thermostat control.[1]

Bill never knew if the new Minnesota company got its idea for an automatic heat regulator from his story. But it didn't matter to him. He realized for the first time, that instead of just making mechanical toys to have fun with, he could invent things that would be useful. He decided to spend his life doing this very thing.

As a grown man Bill Stout encouraged many young people to think original thoughts. "The most satisfying thing a man can do," he said, "is to create things the world has never seen before."

Of his first useful invention, he admitted that he had made it because he had been both uncomfortable and lazy. "Laziness," he smilingly told his friends, "is the mother of invention."

[1] Today thermostats are used in many ways. They control the temperature in buildings and such household appliances as stoves, irons, and refrigerators. They control the water flow in automobile cooling systems and the temperature of airplane motors and instruments.

Counters

To think I once saw grocery shops
  With but a casual eye
And fingered figs and apricots
  As one who came to buy!

To think I never dreamed of how
  Bananas swayed in rain,
And often looked at oranges
  Yet never thought of Spain!

And in those wasted days I saw
  No sails above the tea—
For grocery shops were grocery shops,
  Not hemispheres to me!

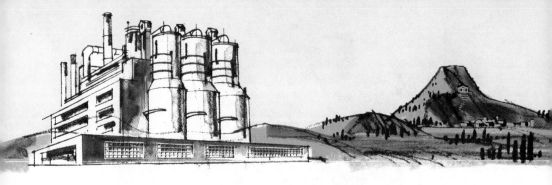

STORY OF SOAP

Throughout history countless inventions and discoveries have gradually improved man's way of life and added to his comfort. Many of these things are so familiar to us that we never stop to think how wonderful they really are. Take, for example, such a common thing as a cake of soap.

Thousands of men and women have worked very hard to bring us soap. Its story takes us to many parts of the world and through many ages.

Life without Soap

Suppose soap suddenly disappeared from the earth. For a few days we probably wouldn't miss it too much. Then we would find that we couldn't keep our hands, clothes, and houses clean. Soon we would begin to feel very uncomfortable. From that time on things could get very bad indeed. Terrible diseases might sweep over the world as they did through Europe in the Middle Ages.

Those who were well enough to work might find their businesses hurt or completely closed. For besides its use as a cleaning material, soap is used in a number of unexpected ways. Without soap we would not have many other comforts of life.

Legends about Soap

The materials from which soap was first made were fats, oils, and ashes from burned wood. No one knows who first learned how to combine these materials.

One legend says that a man from Gaul once used fats and ashes to make an oily hairdressing. One day when he was caught in a rainstorm, suds began to cover his head.

This is probably just a story. Yet it is true that in the language of the Gauls the word for *soap* meant "to give brightness to the hair."

Another legend says that the Romans may have been the first to discover soap. There was a hill outside the city of Rome known as Sapo Hill. On this hill poor people burned animals as offerings to their gods. Both the fat from the animals and the ashes from the wood collected there. When it rained, the water, fat, and ashes ran downhill and seeped through the soft clay on the riverbank below. Soon women learned that this clay made washing easier. So Sapo clay may have been the first soap.

This story may not be true either, but the word "sapo" can be found in the word for soap in many European languages.

Cleaning before Soap

While the poor Romans were placing their offerings on Sapo Hill, the rich Romans were spending much of their time in bathhouses. Since they had no soap to use, taking a bath was almost an all-day job.

First the Romans soaked themselves in very hot water. Then they rubbed their bodies rapidly with a pumice stone. After this the people took a cold-water bath to wash away the dirt.

Next the Romans covered themselves with oil to soften their skin after the hard treatment. Finally they put perfume on their bodies to cover up the odors.

The Romans, of course, could not wash clothing with pumice stones, oils, and perfumes. They had to find another means of getting their clothes clean. An early method used has been preserved in the ruins of the city of Pompeii, which many Romans once visited.

One warm summer day about two thousand years ago, a blinding river of mud and hot ashes suddenly roared down from a nearby volcano. The flowing material soon buried villages and towns for miles around. Under this blanket, undisturbed for about eighteen hundred years, lay the city of Pompeii.

A little over a hundred years ago men who were interested in early civilizations began to dig into the ruins of Pompeii. When the dust was finally cleared away, almost every part of the lives of the people could be studied. Among the shops that were found was that of the fuller.

A fuller was a cleaner of clothes. Today we would call his shop a laundry. Yet a fuller's method of removing dirt from clothes was very different from the method used by present-day laundries.

First one of the fullers would put the clothes into a large kettle of water. Then he would jump up and down on them to loosen some of the dirt.

Next a helper would hang the clothes up in the sunshine to dry.

When the laundry had dried, the dirt which had been loosened was brushed away.

Last of all the clothing was hung on a tentlike frame under which a special fire burned. This whitened the cloth.

The people who studied the ruins of the fuller's shop also discovered a greenish claylike material called fuller's earth. Though this was not soap, it did help remove grease from cloth.

With such methods as these, some people bathed themselves and cleaned their clothes before the discovery of soap.

History of Soap

About a hundred years after the volcano buried Pompeii, a coarse cleaning material was made in France. Then in about the year 700 the Spanish also began to make a soaplike material. And about the year 1200 the people of England started to make soap. Soon groups of soapmakers joined together in Europe and soaps began to be improved. However, only the rich could afford to buy soap.

When a pioneer woman made soap, she used fat she had saved from the dinner table and grease from her cooking. The fat and grease were boiled with lye made from wood ashes. The result of this mixture was a strong yellow soap that was hard on the skin and clothes. Even so it was a big improvement over the cleaning materials of earlier times.

About the year 1800 a man in France found that soda, made from common salt, could be used in making soap. As a result of his studies, soap could be made in greater amounts at less cost. Now the common people could afford to buy soap.

When companies were first formed to manufacture soap in America, they made it in huge outdoor kettles. The boiling mixture was stirred with a wooden board and then poured into wooden frames for hardening. The materials for the soap—the fats and oils—came from inns and private homes.

As the soapmaking business grew and the methods of manufacturing it improved, more fats

and oils were needed. In order to get them, businessmen had to travel farther and farther away from home. Today the needed oils come from plants as well as animals, and are brought from all over the world.

From the South Sea Islands comes coconut oil. Palm oil is brought from the Far East. The Spanish send an oil from olives. From the North and South Poles come fish oils. The flower gardens of France and many other countries give us the oils used to perfume the soap. From the United States come such raw materials as cottonseed oil and peanut oil. Every possible material in the world is studied, as the search for new and better materials to use in soapmaking continues.

Modern Uses of Soap

Today soap plays an important part in our lives in many ways.

It helps keep us clean and free from disease. When we wash, the dirt, bits of dried skin, germs, and body oil stick to the soap and can be washed away. Many diseases caused by germs can be stopped in this way. For example, the use of soap has almost rid the earth of flea-spread diseases. This is true because fleas cannot live on a clean body.

It has been said that soap can protect people from more diseases than any other single thing they can use. Soap will act as a germ killer when it is used in mixtures as weak as one drop of soap to a THOUSAND drops of water. Actually when we wash our hands, we most often use one drop of soap to TWELVE drops of water. In washing dishes or clothing, we normally use about one drop of soap to ONE HUNDRED drops of water.

There are many jobs for soap in businesses, too. It is used in making automobile tires, telephone wires, and many kinds of metal, leather, and cloth goods. Because soap makes things slide smoothly, it is used to roll the thin pieces of metal used for wrapping such things as candy. It is in the oil put on coal to make it dustless. It softens the leather in shoes. Soap removes the grease from wool so that blankets and other woolen goods can be soft, warm, and light in weight. Soap is used in the manufacture of the shiny paper used in some magazines. In many surprising ways soap is at work doing a useful job in business.

Today in the United States alone, companies sell enough soap to provide every person with about twenty-eight pounds of it a year. Soap—the everyday material that we use so unthinkingly—has gradually become a necessity to people in their work and personal well-being.

There are three holes in the bottom of a **coconut** that make it look like a face. *Coco* is Spanish for "a funny face." So a coconut is really a "funny-faced" nut.

Multiple Meanings of Words

Use the glossary below and tell the meaning of the underlined word in the first sentence. Then select a picture which suggests a different meaning for the same word. Continue in the same way with the remaining sentences.

Glossary

bot tle (bot'əl), 1. keep back, control. 2. a container for holding liquids.

carve (kärv), 1. cut into pieces. 2. decorate with designs cut into a surface.

spin (spin), 1. make into thread. 2. turn around rapidly.

trough (trôf), 1. a long, narrow box for holding food or water. 2. a low place between two high places.

Sue will <u>spin</u> the wool and then weave a blanket.
He had to <u>carve</u> flowers on the wooden chest.
<u>Bottle</u> your anger, Martin, and walk quickly away.
It disappeared in the <u>trough</u> between the waves.

SOPERVILLE

My name is Russell Waters, but everybody calls me "Rusty." Whenever my Uncle Wilbur comes for a visit, he makes a big joke about my nickname.

"Hey, Rusty Waters," he always greets me, "how's life in the Red Sea?"

I'm beginning to understand his kind of jokes, so they don't bother me too much. On his last visit, though, Uncle Wilbur earned a nickname, too.

When Uncle Wilbur returned from his vacation last week, he had his usual collection of pictures. Uncle Wilbur, you see, is quite a camera fan. He takes a few slides and snapshots, but his favorites are home movies. His movies are always interesting, and so are the stories he tells about them. After you hear this tale, I'm sure you will agree.

When the family was seated, Uncle Wilbur started the projector. The lights went off, and the show began. The first shot was the title.

We had a good laugh over that. Uncle Wilbur always had trouble with spelling! We knew he meant DESERT, because that's where he had spent his vacation. Still, the word "dessert" seemed to fit, too, for seeing movies after dinner was a very special treat.

The title shot didn't last long and soon we saw a great stretch of sandy desert. Suddenly many little white spots appeared on the screen.

They faded away as the camera focused on a sign.

The next scene showed a small wooden building. Spread out on tables in front of it were many beautiful Indian things for sale. Near the door was a rocking chair. In it a little old Indian was rocking back and forth.

It looked as if Uncle Wilbur had continued grinding the camera as he walked toward the old man, for soon the Indian's picture filled the entire screen. Now we could see that the old fellow was enjoying a cooling bottle of pop.

Uncle Wilbur must have said something about being thirsty on such a hot day, because the camera followed the Indian as he got up to get a bottle of pop for Uncle Wilbur.

Then we saw the desert again and more of those funny white spots on the screen. In between them we could see several big flat hills in the background. Uncle Wilbur told us they were called *mesas*, which means "tables" in Spanish.

The trading post appeared on the screen again. I guess the Indian took this shot, because it showed Uncle Wilbur drinking his bottle of soda pop. He was sitting on a chair with his hat pulled down to shade his eyes from the sun.

The camera must have been turned toward the desert, for the next scene showed those curious white spots once more.

Then the projector clicked off and the lights came on.

While Uncle Wilbur was rewinding the film, I asked him about the white spots. "Say, Uncle Wilbur," I said, "I thought you were on the desert. How do you explain those piles of snow?"

"Snow?" He looked puzzled. Then—"Oh, snow!" And he began to chuckle. "Why, that's not snow, Rusty. That's soap!"

Nobody said anything for a minute. We just looked at him. Then it seemed as if Mom, Dad, and I all breathed at once. "Soap?" we said in chorus.

"Well, that's what the Indian told me when I asked him about it."

We looked at Uncle Wilbur expectantly. It sounded as if a good story were coming. It was! Uncle Wilbur leaned back in his chair and began.

"As the pioneers moved westward, the Indians found that their hunting grounds were disappearing, so the government set aside reservations for them. The movie you just saw showed part of a reservation which came to be known as Soperville.

"Soperville wasn't like any village ever seen before. In fact it probably was the most unusual place in the whole United States. You see, the houses were made of soap! It all came about in a very strange way.

"When the Indians first settled on the reservation, they lived in tents and hunted wild animals just as they had always done.

"On the edge of a flat-topped mesa they cooked the animals that had been killed in their hunts. The fats and oils mixed with the ashes and flowed down to the desert below. Soon a lot of this mixture collected at the base of the mesa. When the pile became large, the Indians moved their fires to

another part of the mesa. Soon there were many piles of this material on the desert floor.

"It occurred to one Indian brave that perhaps he could hollow out one of the piles and make a house for himself. It would protect his family from the cold desert nights better than a tent.

"The brave's idea worked very well. Soon other people on the reservation had hollowed out their own piles of soap.

"Each year quite a few new piles of soap were formed. As the village grew, more homes were hollowed out. In time the Indians even began to carve decorations on the outside of their soap houses.

"It became the custom to have yearly contests to see which family could carve the best design on their home. On the great festival day when the carving was done, dances were held, and a feast was enjoyed. In the evening the chief would present the family who had created the best design with a new bow and arrow.

"Life in Soperville continued quite pleasantly until the awful day of the great disaster.* It

*See history of the word *disaster* on page 341.

rained! Not just a few drops of rain fell, but whole bucketfuls! It rained for days and days.

"Those white spots on the film?" asked Uncle Wilbur as he finished his story—"that's all that is left of Soperville. The whole reservation melted clean away!"

By this time Uncle Wilbur was ready with the next film. But I had another question. "What became of the people?" I asked.

Uncle Wilbur shrugged his shoulders. "Why after all that soap and water they just faded out of the picture. Occasionally, when the light's just right, you can see their shadows moving over the desert floor."

Uncle Wilbur started the next film. Sure enough I could see the shadows among the white spots quite clearly. The trouble was that nothing else was clear. Then suddenly the picture came in focus and the Grand Canyon appeared on the screen. From then on the pictures were pretty good.

Later we got to talking about film editing. That's when you cut out poor frames, add titles, and arrange scenes in an interesting order. I asked my uncle if he'd edited these new films.

"Somewhat," he admitted slowly. "Somewhat."

"Were those white spots and shadows caused by the wrong amount of light?" I asked suspiciously.

Uncle Wilbur simply grinned. So I still don't know if he left those frames in just to make a good story.

I also wondered if the Indian really had told him that story. When I asked Uncle Wilbur, all he said was, "Well, the Indian did say something about the land around there being all washed up."

You can see that Uncle Wilbur is quite a joker. His films are always surprising and his stories are never dull. This year old "Soapy" Waters left us bubbling with laughter!

 The Romans believed that the stars influenced their lives. If they had a **disaster** the "stars" were "against" them. The Italian word *astro* meaning "star" may also be seen in the words astronaut and asterisk.

CHARLOTTE'S WEB*

This is the story of Wilbur, a lovable pig, and of his friend Charlotte, a beautiful large grey spider.

They lived happily in Mr. Homer Zuckerman's barn with Templeton the rat and many other animals.

Every day Fern came to her Uncle Homer's barn to visit with Wilbur. When Wilbur was a tiny, sickly baby pig, Fern had taken care of him. She loved Wilbur very much!

One day the old sheep told Wilbur some disturbing news. "Lurvy, the hired man, and Mr. Zuckerman are fattening you up," she said, "and when it gets cold they are going to kill you for meat!"

---

*Note—This story is a short version of one small part of a complete story for children titled *Charlotte's Web*, by E. B. White; with illustrations by Garth Williams.

Twilight settled over Zuckerman's barn, and a feeling of peace. Fern knew it was almost supper-time but she couldn't bear to leave. Swallows passed on silent wings, in and out of the door-ways, bringing food to their young ones. From across the road a bird sang "Whippoorwill, whip-poorwill!" Lurvy sat down under an apple tree and lit his pipe; the animals sniffed the familiar smell of strong tobacco. Wilbur heard the trill of the tree toad and the occasional slamming of the kitchen door. All these sounds made him feel comfortable and happy, for he loved life and loved to be a part of the world on a summer evening. But as he lay there he remembered what the old sheep had told him. The thought of death came to him and he began to tremble with fear.

"Charlotte?" he said, softly.

"Yes, Wilbur?"

"I don't want to die."

"Of course you don't," said Charlotte in a comforting voice.

"I just love it here in the barn," said Wilbur. "I love everything about this place."

"Of course you do," said Charlotte. "We all do."

The goose appeared, followed by her seven goslings. They thrust their little necks out and kept up a musical whistling, like a tiny troupe of pipers. Wilbur listened to the sound with love in his heart.

"Charlotte?" he said.

"Yes?" said the spider.

"Were you serious when you promised you would keep them from killing me?"

"I was never more serious in my life. I am not going to let you die, Wilbur."

"How are you going to save me?" asked Wilbur, whose curiosity was very strong on this point.

"Well," said Charlotte, vaguely, "I don't really know. But I'm working on a plan."

"That's wonderful," said Wilbur. "How is the plan coming, Charlotte? Have you got very far with it? Is it coming along pretty well?" Wilbur was trembling again, but Charlotte was cool and collected.

"Oh, it's coming all right," she said, lightly. "The plan is still in its early stages and hasn't completely shaped up yet, but I'm working on it."

"When do you work on it?" begged Wilbur.

"When I'm hanging head-down at the top of my web. That's when I do my thinking, because then all the blood is in my head."

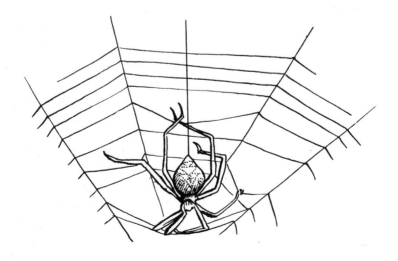

"I'd be only too glad to help in any way I can."

"Oh, I'll work it out alone," said Charlotte. "I can think better if I think alone."

"All right," said Wilbur. "But don't fail to let me know if there's anything I can do to help, no matter how slight."

"Well," replied Charlotte, "you must try to build yourself up. I want you to get plenty of sleep, and stop worrying. Never hurry and never worry! Chew your food thoroughly and eat every bit of it, except you must leave just enough for Templeton. Gain weight and stay well—that's the way you can help. Keep fit, and don't lose your nerve. Do you think you understand?"

"Yes, I understand," said Wilbur.

"Go along to bed, then," said Charlotte. "Sleep is important."

Wilbur trotted over to the darkest corner of his pen and threw himself down. He closed his eyes. In another minute he spoke.

"Charlotte?" he said.

"Yes, Wilbur?"

"May I go out to my trough and see if I left any of my supper? I think I left just a tiny bit of mashed potato."

"Very well," said Charlotte. "But I want you in bed again without delay."

Wilbur started to race out to his yard.

"Slowly, slowly!" said Charlotte. "Never hurry and never worry!"

Wilbur checked himself and crept slowly to his trough. He found a bit of potato, chewed it carefully, swallowed it, and walked back to bed. He closed his eyes and was silent for a while.

"Charlotte?" he said, in a whisper.

"Yes?"

"May I get a drink of milk? I think there are a few drops of milk left in my trough."

"No, the trough is dry, and I want you to go to sleep. No more talking! Close your eyes and go to sleep!"

Wilbur shut his eyes. Fern got up from her stool and started for home, her mind full of everything she had seen and heard.

"Good night, Charlotte!" said Wilbur.

"Good night, Wilbur!"

There was a pause.

"Good night, Charlotte!"

"Good night, Wilbur!"

"Good night!"

"Good night!"

. . .

Astride her web, Charlotte sat moodily eating a horsefly and thinking about the future. After a while she bestirred herself.

She descended to the center of the web and there she began to cut some of her lines. She

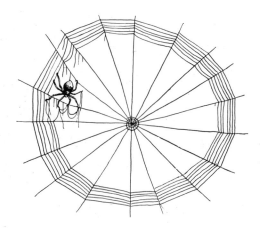

worked slowly but steadily while the other creatures drowsed. None of the others, not even the goose, noticed that she was at work. Deep in his soft bed, Wilbur snoozed. Over in their favorite corner, the goslings whistled a night song.

Charlotte tore quite a section out of her web, leaving an open space in the middle. Then she started weaving something to take the place of the threads she had removed. When Templeton got back from the dump, around midnight, the spider was still at work.

. . .

The next day was foggy. Everything on the farm was dripping wet. The grass looked like a magic carpet. The asparagus patch looked like a silver forest.

On foggy mornings, Charlotte's web was truly a thing of beauty. This morning each thin strand was decorated with dozens of tiny beads of water. The web glistened in the light and made a pattern of loveliness and mystery, like a delicate veil. Even Lurvy, who wasn't particularly interested in beauty, noticed the web when he came with the pig's breakfast. He noted how clearly it showed up and he noted how big and carefully built it

was. And then he took another look and he saw
something that made him set his pail down. There,
in the center of the web, neatly woven in block
letters, was a message. It said:

SOME PIG!

Lurvy felt weak. He brushed his hand across
his eyes and stared harder at Charlotte's web.

"I'm seeing things," he whispered. He dropped
to his knees and uttered a short prayer. Then,
forgetting all about Wilbur's breakfast, he walked
back to the house and called Mr. Zuckerman.

"I think you'd better come down to the pig-pen," he said.

"What's the trouble?" asked Mr. Zuckerman. "Anything wrong with the pig?"

"N-not exactly," said Lurvy. "Come and see for yourself."

The two men walked silently down to Wilbur's yard. Lurvy pointed to the spider's web. "Do you see what I see?" he asked.

Zuckerman stared at the writing on the web. Then he murmured the words "Some Pig." Then he looked at Lurvy. Then they both began to tremble. Charlotte, sleepy after her night's exertions, smiled as she watched. Wilbur came and stood directly under the web.

"Some pig!" muttered Lurvy in a low voice.

"Some pig!" whispered Mr. Zuckerman. They stared and stared for a long time at Wilbur. Then they stared at Charlotte.

"You don't suppose that that spider . . ." began Mr. Zuckerman—but he shook his head and didn't finish the sentence. Instead, he walked solemnly back up to the house and spoke to his wife. "Edith, something has happened," he said, in a weak voice. He went into the living room and sat down, and Mrs. Zuckerman followed.

"I've got something to tell you, Edith," he said. "You better sit down."

Mrs. Zuckerman sank into a chair. She looked pale and frightened.

"Edith," he said, trying to keep his voice steady, "I think you had best be told that we have a very unusual pig."

A look of complete bewilderment came over Mrs. Zuckerman's face. "Homer Zuckerman, what in the world are you talking about?" she said.

"This is a very serious thing, Edith," he replied. "Our pig is completely out of the ordinary."

"What's unusual about the pig?" asked Mrs. Zuckerman, who was beginning to recover from her scare.

"Well, I don't really know yet," said Mr. Zuckerman. "But we have received a sign, Edith —a mysterious sign. A miracle has happened on this farm. There is a large spider's web in the doorway of the barn cellar, right over the pigpen, and when Lurvy went to feed the pig this morning, he noticed the web because it was foggy, and you know how a spider's web looks very distinct in a fog. And right spang in the middle of the web there were the words 'Some Pig.' The words were woven right into the web. They were actually part of the web, Edith. I know, because I have been down there and seen them. It says, 'Some Pig,' just as clear as clear can be. There can be no mistake about it. A miracle has happened and a sign has occurred here on earth, right on our farm, and we have no ordinary pig."

"Well," said Mrs. Zuckerman, "it seems to me you're a little off. It seems to me we have no ordinary *spider*."

"Oh, no," said Zuckerman. "It's the pig that's unusual. It says so, right there in the middle of the web."

"Maybe so," said Mrs. Zuckerman. "Just the same, I intend to have a look at that spider."

"It's just a common grey spider," said Zuckerman.

They got up, and together they walked down to Wilbur's yard. "You see, Edith? It's just a common grey spider."

Wilbur was pleased to receive so much attention. Lurvy was still standing there, and Mr. and Mrs. Zuckerman, all three, stood for about an hour, reading the words on the web over and over, and watching Wilbur.

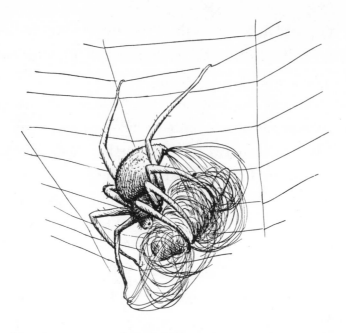

Charlotte was delighted with the way her trick was working. She sat without moving a muscle, and listened to the conversation of the people. When a small fly blundered into the web, just beyond the word "pig," Charlotte dropped quickly down, rolled the fly up, and carried it out of the way.

After a while the fog lifted. The web dried off and the words didn't show up so plainly. The Zuckermans and Lurvy walked back to the house. Just before they left the pigpen, Mr. Zuckerman took one last look at Wilbur.

"You know," he said, in an important voice, "I've thought all along that that pig of ours was an extra good one. He's a solid pig. That pig is as solid as they come. You notice how solid he is around the shoulders, Lurvy?"

"Sure. Sure I do," said Lurvy. "I've always noticed that pig. He's quite a pig."

"He's long, and he's smooth," said Zuckerman.

"That's right," agreed Lurvy. "He's as smooth as they come. He's some pig."

Tracing Word Meanings

A dictionary may use several words or phrases to define a word. If you do not understand the first meaning given for a word, read until you find a meaning you know.

Read the following sentences. Then read the definitions for the underlined words.

How could they scoff at that art work?

Sam felt remorse because he had failed to keep his promise.

Did Androcles plead for his freedom?

plead (plēd), entreat, implore,
   beseech, beg
re morse (ri môrs'), contrition,
   repentance, regret, deep sorrow
scoff (skôf), mock, jibe, jeer,
   sneer, make fun of

Reread the sentences. For each underlined word, substitute a meaning you know. To make sense, a word in the first sentence given for rereading may need to be omitted.

THE WEAVER

Among all the Greeks no one could spin and weave quite so well as Arachne. People would come from far and near to watch her work and to gaze in wonder at her skill.

Not only was her finished work beautiful to see, but the speed and grace of her movements amazed those who watched her. "Surely you were taught by the goddess Athena!" they would exclaim.

Though these words were meant to please Arachne, they only made her angry. No one had taught her—certainly not the goddess of weaving. Her skill had come from hours and hours of practice when all the other girls had been out playing.

Besides, she wondered if even the goddess Athena could weave as well as she.

One day after she had finished a particularly lovely piece of weaving, Arachne bragged to the onlookers, "Not even Athena could do such perfect work."

Now it happened that Athena, disguised as a little old woman, had been watching. She came forward saying, "My child, you do have most unusual ability, but you must not compare yourself with a goddess. You will make Athena angry. You should ask her forgiveness for such proud bragging."

"Is that so!" Arachne scoffed. "Then let Athena prove that she is better. If she wins in a contest, there is no punishment that I will not endure. Let her appear, if she dares."

"She is here!" cried the goddess throwing off her disguise. There stood Athena in a shining white robe decorated with strands of gold and silver. Everyone bowed low—everyone except Arachne who was too proud to plead for Athena's forgiveness. Arachne foolishly meant to have either victory or death. The goddess, seeing this, delayed no longer but said, "Let the trial begin."

On her web Athena wove scenes showing the greatness of the gods. As a special warning to Arachne, the goddess showed what had happened to humans who had displeased the gods. Around the edge of the design she patterned her own tree —the peaceful olive. Her work was so beautiful that the watchers sighed in admiration.

Arachne, too, wove stories of the gods, but her pictures focused on their weaknesses and mistakes. Around the edge she put a difficult combination of colorful flowers.

At last the two weavers completed their work, and the expectant crowd quickly moved forward to study the results.

Arachne's creatures were so lifelike that they literally appeared to talk and move about. But Athena had put a glow of lightning and fire in her work that went beyond the ability of man. Even Arachne could see that her own work could not compare with the delicate shadings and perfect balance of Athena's. The gray eyes of the goddess flashed as she gazed at the insult to the gods that Arachne had woven. She seized the insulting web and in one stroke rent it to pieces. Then three times she touched Arachne's forehead until the girl shuddered with shame.

The high-spirited girl could stand the disgrace
no longer. In remorse she rushed from the scene
and hanged herself.

But Athena did not want to see such skill taken
from the earth. Before Arachne was completely
drained of life, Athena raised her powerful voice
and declared, "You shall be permitted to live on,
shameless girl, but in a different form. You and
your kind shall remain forever spinning and hanging from a web."

Even as the words were uttered, Arachne began to change. Her arms and legs grew thinner, her head and body became quite small, her hair fell off, and her skillful fingers stuck to her sides as legs.

Arachne, the spider, may still be seen working at her delicate web as she spins the silver thread to which she often hangs.

"Arachnid" is the name given to a member of a class of animals to which spiders belong. The name comes from **Arachne**, the spinner told about in this Greek myth.

Unit Six

Ways of the Weather

Word Meaning from a Paragraph

When you discover the meaning of a word from the sense of a paragraph, you use a context, or meaning, clue.

Read the following paragraphs. Then tell in your own words the meaning of each underlined word.

1. The dark skies, strong winds, and huge waves were frightening. Suddenly the ship radio burst to life . . . *heavy storm warnings* . . . *winds clocked at ninety miles an hour*. The captain worked quickly to change course before the hurricane hit.

2. As he walked along, Jerry breathed through his handkerchief. He had to protect himself from the dusty, dry air. Everywhere the grass was brown and the flowers were dying. "Nothing will be alive if the drought doesn't end soon!" he gasped.

3. "Someone has taken the bombs out of the cave!" shouted the major. As he peered deeply into the darkness, he discovered that the TNT and the sticks of dynamite were gone, too! He pounded his fist angrily, dashed out of the cave, and ordered his men to search for the missing explosives.

Check your word meanings in the Glossary.

Families Escape Floods

CINCINNATI, Ma
The Red Cross came t
today of families le:
less when the Ohi
reached flood level a:
of melting snow a

Fog Grounds Planes

SAN DIEGO, December 14—
The airport here was closed
for four hours this mornin
n heavy fog blanketed th
Flights were resumed aft

DROUGHT RUINS CROPS

WA CITY, July 4—Many
western farmers expect
losses this year because
nage to corn crops from

Snow Stops Traffic

BOSTON, Feb. 18—A bli
zard snarled traffic during t
rush hour today, causing ma
accidents and bringing cars
a standstill.

Ball Game Rained Out

ST. LOUIS, May 1—Many
baseball fans were disap-
pointed today when the game
was called in the third inning

HEAT WAVE
TAKES LIVES

OS ANGELES, October
— Five deaths this week
been attributed to the
one hundred degree
eratures which continue

WEATHER CONTROL

Newspaper headlines such as these remind us of how important the weather is to us. It has an effect upon sports, travel, crops, health, and our very lives. No wonder everyone talks and writes about the weather!

In many ways man has been able to ADJUST to the forces of weather. He has learned to clothe his body and build homes for protection. He has built dams to control floodwaters. He has learned how to bring water to dry lands. He has developed

means of forecasting so he may be prepared for the weather, but he has not been able to do much about changing it.

How much better it might be if man could learn to CONTROL weather forces! Suppose rain could be made to fall only when and where it was needed! How nice it would be if the poles could be made warmer and hot areas cooler! Such control is now the goal of many people interested in the science of weather.

From earliest times man has known that his well-being depended upon the weather. Yet for many years it was commonly believed that the gods controlled the forces of weather and, therefore, man could do nothing about them.

About twenty-three hundred years ago some people began to suspect that weather forces were the result of natural laws. The first careful study of weather was made about then.

A Greek named Aristotle was one of the greatest thinkers of his time. He ran his own school and privately taught Alexander the Great. Aristotle wrote about many subjects. His book about the weather was called *Meteorologica*, which meant "above the earth." From this word we get our name for the science of weather—meteorology.

Aristotle's book, however, did not make meteorology a science. The instruments needed for study had not been invented. In fact, it was not until almost two thousand years later that such instruments began to be developed.

The study of weather as a science began with a man from Italy, whom we call by his first name, Galileo. He was born in 1564, nearly nineteen hundred years after Aristotle. Galileo was interested in many things, including the weather. One of his important inventions was the thermometer which made it possible to measure temperature carefully.

From Galileo's time on, many instruments were developed to measure weather changes. Then with the invention of the telegraph in 1844 these changes, in the form of weather reports, could be sent to, and received from, other areas. By the late 1800's many countries had set up systems of daily weather study and forecasts.

Since the 1800's meteorologists have learned much about weather forces, and their forecasts have contained fewer mistakes. These scientists are also learning about the causes of weather.

We live at the bottom of an ocean of air that is over three hundred miles deep. Most of our weather develops within ten miles of the earth's surface. Here the air is full of water vapor that causes such things as clouds, rain, and fog. Air currents flow and bump into each other, carrying the water vapor from place to place. This brings the weather changes.

These weather changes do not always occur where and when we want them to. Some people have thought that, by controlling the amount of water vapor in the air, droughts and floods could be stopped. Rain might be made to fall where it was needed.

In 1899 the American government set aside $100,000 for rainmaking experiments. Some people suggested that perhaps a loud noise would shake the water droplets in the clouds. These droplets would then bump into each other, grow larger, and finally fall as rain or snow.

During the first test, explosives were set off all day and night. The countryside shook for miles around. And it did rain! But meteorologists would not believe that the explosions had caused it. The experiment proved nothing.

A second test was made. This time cannons were shot off, and then explosives. Also, balloons were sent up carrying explosives which were set off in the clouds. For two weeks the noise continued. Again it rained. Again scientists were sure it would have rained anyway.

The story was reported in the newspapers. Suddenly many rainmakers appeared on the scene and promised farmers rain. To bring this about they used many devices.

A rainmaker might arrive at a farmhouse and say that, for one hundred dollars, he could make it rain in a week's time. Then he would mutter some magic words, or heat chemicals which would send gases into the air. If rain fell within the given time, he would claim that he had been the cause of it. If not, he would quickly disappear.

Finally, in 1946, a scientific experiment was tried. Dry ice was dropped into some clouds from an airplane. In about twenty minutes people on the ground saw the clouds begin to disappear. A light snow started to fall!

When the news was reported there was a lot of excitement. People on mountaintops threw dry ice at clouds. Airplane pilots eagerly seeded clouds. But it was soon found that while the clouds would often disappear, they could not often be made to drop rain or snow. This was because only certain clouds, at certain temperatures, could be used. Only scientists knew which these were.

In the last few years other materials have been used in rainmaking experiments. But even though progress has been made, it is still true that scientific rainmaking can be done only when clouds are present. Even then they must be special kinds of clouds that are almost ready to form rain anyway.

Of course, rain that makes a farmer happy may ruin a ski area or ground some airplanes. Trying to please everyone is a difficult problem. In the future, laws may have to be passed to govern such weather control.

While scientists continue to search for means of making rain, they are also studying ways to control other weather forces.

Strong winds, such as hurricanes, cause much damage every year. In 1947 dry ice was poured into a hurricane near Florida. Right away more rain poured down. Then the hurricane made a sharp turn and caused much damage on land. Would it have turned anyway? No one can say. Experiments are being continued, but carefully.

Some meteorologists would like to change temperatures in parts of the world. Several ways have been suggested to make areas cooler or warmer.

In sections of New England and Canada, 1816 was known as the "Year-without-a-Summer." Though the whole world endured cold spells, winter simply wouldn't leave that area. Snow fell all summer, ruining many crops. What caused it? Scientists aren't sure, but they have an idea.

The spring before, a volcano boiled forth on the other side of the world. A huge dust cloud formed. Perhaps it was unusually thick over New England and Canada. It is suggested that the cloud caused some of the sun's heat to be sent back into space, making temperatures cooler.

Some scientists think that if several tons of dust were dropped from a plane over hot areas, temperatures could be cooled as much as fifteen degrees. If so, the hot parts of the world might be made cool.

A different effect might take place if dust were dropped on the ice and snow near the North Pole. The dust would soak up the sun's heat, the snow could then melt, and the area would be made warmer. The danger is that floods might result.

Another idea for warming the North Pole is to dam the waterway between Alaska and Asia. A warm current of water would then flow into the ocean around the waterway and melt the ice cover. This, however, would raise the level of other oceans so much that large sections of land would be flooded.

Scientists agree that before man causes any temperature changes to be made, the world-wide effects must be carefully studied.

Much of the beauty of life comes from the air. Everyone enjoys the deep blue of a summer sky or a glowing sunset. Though the weather is not always friendly, we must remember that it develops in our ocean of air. And air is the very breath of life. The earth is the only body in our solar system with the right kind and amount of air for life as we know it. Once we learn the laws of the weather that is made in our air, we may be able to protect ourselves from its damaging effects.

If man uses carefully the discoveries made since the time of Aristotle, and the discoveries of the future, he will be able to live a better life. But man has much to learn before his dream of controlling the weather can come true. Yet some-day, a future meteorologist may find the key.

The Latin word for 100 was *centum,* and a *centuria* was a company of 100 soldiers. Our word **century** has come to mean any sequence of 100—especially 100 years. What does the word cent mean?

Snow in the City

Snow is out of fashion,
    But it still comes down,
To whiten all the buildings
    In our town;
To dull the noise of traffic;
    To dim each glaring light
With star-shaped feathers
    Of frosty white.
And not the tallest building
    Halfway up the sky;
Or all the trains and buses,
    And taxis scudding by;
And not a million people,
    Not one of them at all,
Can do a thing about the snow
    But let it fall!

Word Meaning from a Sentence

A group of words in a sentence may give you a context clue to the meaning of an unknown word.

In each of the three sentences which follow, what words define the underlined word?

1. She is a good observer because she looks at things carefully.

2. Since the men have been trained to work together, they make a good crew.

3. An aeronaut enjoys sailing through the air.

Sometimes you can discover the meaning of a word by thinking about the situation described in the sentence.

What do you think each underlined word means in the sentences below?

1. Since Bill only skinned his knee, his fall wasn't a serious casualty.

2. I stared in dismay when the tightrope walker slipped and fell.

3. The button, which had been dangling from a thread, was now fastened tightly.

Check your word meanings in the Glossary.

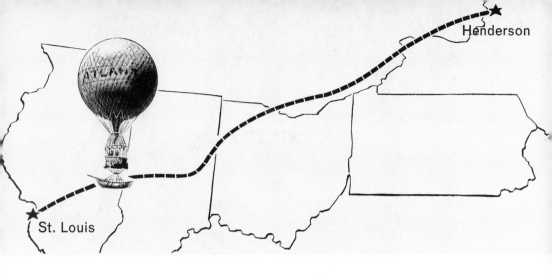

St. Louis

Henderson

PIONEER AERONAUT

The balloon floated a mile above the ground. In the basket hanging below it were John Wise, the owner of the balloon, and his passenger, a rich businessman. The two men went on talking as the balloon continued to rise.

"So you see, Mr. Gager, we can change the direction in which we are traveling by letting out some gas. In this way we can control our height until we hit a stream of air that is flowing the way we wish to go." As he spoke, Wise showed how this could be done. The balloon changed its course.

"Do you mean to say," Mr. Gager exclaimed, "that the air is full of currents going in different directions?"

"Yes, if we are below a certain height," Mr. Wise agreed. "However, I have discovered that if

the balloon sails above 12,000 feet, it will always
travel to the east. At that level there is a great
river of air. It flows from the west to the east.
ALWAYS!"

John Wise grew excited as he always did when he
thought about that river of air. It had given him
a wonderful idea, but to make it work he needed
the help of Oliver Gager.

It was Wise's hope that huge balloons could be built that would be able to carry people and freight across the country and even over the ocean to Europe, by riding the river of air. Then the balloons could be shipped back to their starting point. This hope had led to his idea to form a Trans-Atlantic Balloon Company. If all went well, perhaps Mr. Gager would agree to provide part of the money needed for such a venture. Finally, at 8,000 feet up, the businessman said, "Count me in!" Wise lost no time in returning to the ground.

Some days later the two men met again.

"We must make people believe that your river of air is actually there. Otherwise they won't wish to support our company," Mr. Gager said.

Wise thought about it for a minute. "Perhaps we could put ads in the newspaper," he suggested.

"No, no," Gager disagreed. "We have to do something spectacular, something that will put our company's name on everybody's lips."

"Well," said Wise, "suppose we build one huge balloon. We could fly it from St. Louis in the west to New York in the east by using the river of air. As we pass over cities we could call greetings to the people below. That certainly should be spectacular!"

"That's a good idea," agreed Mr. Gager. "And gather a crew while the balloon is being built." He grinned as he added, "Please be sure to save a place for me."

Right away Wise began to make plans for the flight. The balloon would be the biggest one ever built. It would carry the latest scientific instruments. So that people would know what he wanted to use it for someday, he decided to name the balloon "Atlantic."

The trial run was set for July 1, 1859. As the day approached, Wise began to worry that the newspaper reports would treat the flight as just another circus act. In the last few years many balloonists, in order to earn money, had put on shows. They went up hanging by their teeth or throwing out fireworks. One man had even gone up astride a horse!

To make sure his flight would be recognized as a scientific venture, Wise was careful in choosing his crew. John LaMountane, who built the balloon, would go along as pilot. Oliver Gager would serve as scientific observer, and a Mr. Hyde, from a St. Louis newspaper, would travel as reporter. To prove that the trip could serve a useful purpose,

Wise made arrangements to carry mail. For the first time letters and newspapers would be sent by air mail.

The weather on the first of July was perfect. Families from miles around went to St. Louis to watch the balloon take off. It took all day to fill it with gas, for it was large enough to cover a five-story building. A basket car hung below it. Under that was a lifeboat. The plans were for the four passengers to ride in the car. However, by the time everything was loaded there was room for only two. LaMountane and Gager had to ride in the lifeboat.

At 6:45 in the evening the ropes that held the Atlantic were cut. The balloon rose gradually and gracefully and then swung off to the east. From then on nothing seemed to go right.

With dismay Wise noticed that the ropes which supported the car and lifeboat were not even. Six of the thirty-six ropes were shorter than they should have been. Not only were they carrying the entire weight, but they were cutting into the balloon. Wise called down to the men in the lifeboat. LaMountane was feeling ill, so Gager agreed to climb up and help Wise adjust the ropes. It was

a difficult and dangerous thing to do. Their fingers were raw and blistered before they had finished.

Soon night came. Wise called down to the others and told them he was going to take a nap. Then he checked the hose from which gas escaped when the balloon became too full. It was where it should be—hanging over the side of the car. Wise curled up and fell asleep.

For a while the trip continued uneventfully. Then Gager decided the balloon was rising too slowly. He threw some sand over the side to make it lighter. Too quickly the balloon shot up. In the thinner air, the bag swelled. The hose was drawn into the car where it came to rest in front of Wise's face. His breathing grew heavier.

The three men became frightened by the fast rise and called to Wise. There was no answer. It was then that Hyde turned to look at the sleeping man. At once he pulled the hose away, realizing that breathing the poisonous gas could kill a man. He slapped the aeronaut awake. Somehow Wise managed to steady himself enough to let the right amount of gas escape from the balloon. It descended to a more comfortable level. When they were sailing smoothly along once more, Wise turned to

Hyde and grinned. "That was a wonderful dream I was having. It was all about an interplanetary balloon trip. It's too bad you had to wake me!"

By morning they were floating over the Great Lakes. Everything looked peaceful. Leaning over the edge, the men waved to astonished people in sailing ships below. Suddenly the balloon picked up speed. Wise noticed that it was the kind of wind that gave rise to fierce storms in the summertime. Heavy clouds rolled along. Then—he saw the tempest. They were heading right into it!

"Throw over more sand," Wise called. "Maybe we can rise above it!"

"The sand's almost gone!" Gager called back.

"Then throw over everything you can grab hold of—even the food!"

As they did so, the big balloon began to rise. The men in the lifeboat climbed up to the car. LaMountane began cutting the ropes that held the lifeboat. Three of the lines were loosened when the balloon suddenly plunged downward again. It dropped to a few feet above the water. The lifeboat filled. Then a sharp updraft raised the balloon several hundred feet into the air. Water poured out of the lifeboat as it twisted and turned,

dangling from a single rope. Wise set the boat free
and then hung on tightly. Any second now he
expected to be dashed into the water. It never
happened. The storm disappeared as quickly as it
had come.

When the men again looked over the side, they were amazed to see a forest below them. The balloon sailed on, breaking off huge branches as if they were matchsticks. Finally it crashed into a tall tree. The bag split open and freed the gas. The car dangled about sixty feet above the ground.

People who had seen the crazy flight gathered below to stare in amazement. One very proper old lady adjusted her glasses for a better look and then shook a finger at the men. "You look

like a sensible group," she scolded. "What do you mean by soaring about in such a silly vehicle?" Then she laughed and added, "You could probably stand a good meal. Will you come home with me for dinner?"

The astonished men thanked her, and somehow managed to climb down the tree to the ground. John Wise then straightened his shoulders and announced to the onlookers: "Good people, you have just seen the end of the longest balloon trip in history."

As the people clapped and cheered, the four travelers set off with the old woman.

The next day many newspapers carried the story. They called it the greatest balloon flight ever made. In nineteen hours and fifty minutes the men had traveled from St. Louis to Henderson, New York. It was a distance of almost one thousand miles!

It was a miracle that anyone lived through the wild flight of the Atlantic, but luckily the only casualty was the Trans-Atlantic Balloon Company. No one at that time would support a flight across the ocean. Among the Atlantic's crew, John Wise was the only one who continued to make many flights. Finally, at the age of seventy-one, he made his 446th flight. He soared over Lake Michigan and disappeared.

After his death many reporters wrote about his contributions to what man knew about the air. In particular they wrote about his discovery of the west to east river of air. However, people soon forgot about this current. Not until World War II did American pilots rediscover it. They called it the jet stream. Today knowing the speed and the position of the jet stream helps meteorologists in weather forecasting. They know that certain kinds of storms usually occur below it. It also helps airplane pilots. By riding it, travel time from west to east can be shortened.

Even though John Wise never realized his dream of transatlantic flight, later men did. Their success was due in large measure to the scientific contributions made by John Wise, one of America's first great aeronauts.

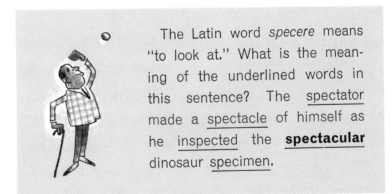

The Latin word *specere* means "to look at." What is the meaning of the underlined words in this sentence? The spectator made a spectacle of himself as he inspected the **spectacular** dinosaur specimen.

Word Meaning from Another Word

In some sentences a synonym for an unknown word may help to explain its meaning.

Find the synonym for the underlined word in each of the next six sentences.

1. That voyage is a long journey across the sea.
2. The spinning top slowly stopped whirling.
3. Our guest will be the visitor from Asia.
4. If the pears rot, the peaches may decay, too.
5. The flaming sun looked like a fiery ball.
6. The tall stone post looked like a pillar.

Check the Glossary for another synonym for each of the words underlined above.

In some sentences an antonym for an unknown word may help to explain its meaning.

Find the antonym for each underlined word in the following sentences.

1. The pond was shallow but the lake was deep.
2. Our allies helped us fight our enemies.
3. At first he was boastful; later he was modest.
4. The gloomy losers left the cheerful winners.
5. Some are scolded, while others are praised.

A TRUE HISTORY

About the year A.D. 160, over 1800 years ago, a Greek named Lucian wrote the very first tale of interplanetary travel. He said that his purpose in writing it was to make fun of the tall travel tales about fabulous creatures in fabulous lands that were popular in his time. Lucian said that he could tell the tallest tale of all— but, unlike other writers, he wanted the reader to know that not a word of his story was true.

Many of the scientific beliefs of his time were reflected in Lucian's story. Earlier people had believed that the heavenly bodies were gods and goddesses. The very idea that there even *were* other worlds to visit originated with the Greeks. If, as some said, the moon *was* another world, then someday people should be able to go there. And, since no one could imagine an end to the air, breathing in space should be no problem. Weather forces could conceivably aid interplanetary travel. Upon reaching the moon, travelers would most likely find life there. For otherwise, that "planet" would have been created for no purpose.

Although Lucian didn't say so, he was probably also making fun of many of these beliefs when he wrote A TRUE HISTORY.

With a crew of 50 daring men I set sail in my new ship. I was undertaking the voyage because I had a curious mind and wished for new adventures. In particular I wanted to learn how wide was the ocean and what sort of people lived on the other side of it.

By noon we had left the shore behind and were in the unexplored part of the sea, where anything could happen. Soon our ship was caught in a fierce storm. The hurricane turned the ship around three times and then lifted it about 350 miles into the air. With sails full we were carried higher and higher above the clouds.

For seven days and nights we traveled through the sky. On the eighth day we came in view of a sort of earth in the air. It looked like a large, round island and it seemed to shine with a very bright light.

When we neared it, we dropped anchor and went ashore. We began to explore the countryside. It was not long before we met with a number of men. They were riding vultures in the same way that we ride horses. For the most part, the vultures had three heads and were very large. Their size may be imagined by this—each feather on their wings

was longer and thicker than the mast of a tall
ship. It was the duty of the men who rode the
vultures to police the island. Whenever they
found a stranger, they carried him before the king.
We could do nothing but go with them.

As soon as the king saw us he said, "I see by
your clothes that you are Greeks."

"This is so," I agreed.

"How did you manage to travel through so much
air?" he asked.

I told him of our adventures. He then began to tell us some of his.

"I, too," he said, "am a Greek—the same Endymion who, according to legend, was loved by the moon goddess." (She had seen him while he tended his flock of sheep. So that she might spend each evening in his company, she had cast a spell of lasting sleep over him.) "What the legend does not tell is that one night, as I lay sleeping, the moon goddess spirited me away from the earth. She brought me to this great country in the air and made me the king. This country you are visiting is the moon!"

Endymion went on to say that we would be his guests and would be provided with every necessity. He added that we would live the happiest of lives with him when the war was over.

Much surprised to hear of a war, I asked who could possibly be his enemy. To this Endymion replied, "We are fighting the people of the sun. The contest began because we wished to send our poor people to form a settlement on Venus, which is a wild, bare land. To this Phaeton, the king of the sun, would not agree because he was upset that he had not thought of it first. He met us with an army and we, who had no weapons with us, were forced to return home. However, I am quite determined to plant a colony on Venus. If you would like to help us, I will give you vultures and weapons. Tomorrow we begin the march."

"Endymion, we would be most pleased to join you," I replied.

The next morning we were told that the army of the sun was approaching. The army of the moon made ready for battle. There were 80,000 men mounted on vultures and 20,000 more rode Cabbage Birds. There were many such birds on the moon. Instead of feathers they had cabbages. For wings they had large lettuce leaves.

Besides these troops there were 30,000 Flea Guards, mounted on fleas that were twelve times as big as an elephant; and 50,000 Wind Coursers, who held long robes up to the wind and sailed through the air like ships. There were also a great many Garlic Throwers and Bean Shooters.

Endymion's army also included 60,000,000 foot soldiers. These men were backed up by spiders, each as big as an island. It was the duty of the spiders to fill the air between the moon and Venus with a huge web. This served as a floor for the foot soldiers to march on.

The army of the sun was just as striking. On the left wing, led by Phaeton himself, was the Ant Army. Nearly 50,000 men were mounted on flying ants, each about 200 feet long. These ants helped the men by fighting with their horns.

On the right wing were 50,000 Gnat Riders mounted on giant gnats. Behind them were the Radish Throwers who were armed with poisonous radishes, and the Mushroom Fighters who used asparagus plants for weapons.

Both armies were backed up by troops from other stars in the Milky Way.

The signal was given to begin, and the battle raged back and forth through the heavens. Finally the army of the moon began to gain ground. It seemed that victory for them was near. Then more troops from distant stars came to the aid of Phaeton's army. The army of the moon quickly fell back in wild disorder. Endymion was chased to the very door of the capital and two of my friends and I were captured. Our hands were tied with spider webs and, together with other prisoners, we were carried to the sun.

Phaeton did not care to take over the moon. Instead he put a thick wall of clouds between the sun and moon. This meant that the moon at once lost all sunlight and was sentenced to continual darkness. Endymion begged Phaeton to remove the cloud wall. This the sun god agreed to do if Endymion would agree to the following treaty.

The sun and its allies, and the moon and its allies, have entered into the following agreement. The sun will remove the wall and stop making attacks on the moon. Both sides will free prisoners on the payment of a fair price. The moon will not trespass upon the rights of any stars. Also it will not enter into war with the sun. Instead, the two powers shall help each other if a third power should attack one of them. The king of the moon also agrees to pay the king of the sun a yearly amount of 10,000 barrels of dew. To make sure this is done, he also agrees to give the sun 10,000 hostages. As to the colony on Venus, both powers shall help found it. This treaty shall be written on a yellow pillar that will be put up between the moon and the sun.

When this peace treaty was signed, the wall of clouds was torn down and prisoners were exchanged. When my two friends and I again reached the moon, my other sailors and Endymion himself came to meet us. Endymion suggested that we settle down on the moon or else become a part of the colony on Venus, as we wished. However, by this time we were eager to return home. Seeing this, Endymion agreed to return us to the earth after we had feasted with him for a week.

Before I leave the story of the moon, I must tell you of the things I observed during the week of feasting.

When a moonman grows old he does not die as we do, but simply disappears in the air like smoke.

Everyone eats the same kind of food. They roast flying frogs on coals. Then they sit around a large table and breathe the smoke from the fire. They live only on the smoke.

Everyone there who is thought to be good-looking is baldheaded, but bearded. Each foot is in one piece for they have no toes. All of the people have cabbages for tails. These never break off even when a man falls down on them.

As to their clothing, the rich people wear robes made of glass, while the poor people must use brass. The moon is very rich in ores.

I also saw one unusual thing in the king's palace. It was a huge mirror lying over a shallow well. Anyone who went down into the well could hear everything that was said on the earth. If he looked

in the mirror he could see all of the cities on the
earth. One time I saw my family and my whole
country, but I cannot say if they saw me.

At the end of the week we made ready to leave
and boarded our ship. The king, Endymion, gave
me a parting present of two glass and five brass
robes, together with a suit of armor made of bean

shells. He also sent 1,000 vultures to guide us on the first 500 miles of our trip.

On the return voyage we stopped at Venus, where we saw the first colonists hard at work. Then, after being carried for three days by the winds of heaven, we approached the earth. Even though we could see the ocean quite clearly, we could make out no land except for the islands in the air that seemed to be very fiery and sparkling. On the fourth day, around noon, the wind grew calm and we were settled gently upon the seas of Earth.

He who does not believe this adventure may go to the moon himself and see with his own eyes that everything I have said is true.

Braille writing is embossed or raised. *Embossed* comes from a French word meaning "a swelling upon." Our own word **cabbage** comes from a form of that same French word meaning "a swollen head."

OTHER PEOPLE'S WEATHER

Big Steve, the double-quick tunnelman, is a new tall-tale hero. With his rock hog, Daisy—a cross between a dog, a ground hog, a mole, and a gopher —he roamed the United States digging tunnels and benefiting mankind.

Febold Feboldson, the weather control expert of Nebraska, sat down on the grass next to his visitor. "I sure would like to do something about the weather in Nebraska," he said.

"What's the matter with it?" asked his guest.

"Oh, too cold in the winter, too hot in the summer. What I'd like to do is get some of that good Florida weather in here, at least in the winter. But I can't think of a way to do it."

The visitor chewed thoughtfully on a piece of grass while he rubbed the animal beside him between the ears. Then he said, "You can always pipe it in."

At this, Febold opened his mouth, stared at him, and finally said, "Say that again."

"Pipe it in."

"Well, I'll be!" shouted Febold slapping his leg. Then on second thought he said, "Sure, but who's going to lay all that pipe?"

"You don't need any pipe. Just bore a small tunnel and—"

"What business did you say you were in?" interrupted Febold.

"I bore tunnels. I'm Big Steve, the tunnelman."

"Well, I'll be!" cried Febold. "You're just the man for me!"

That night, at Febold's, Big Steve studied a map of the United States. Then turning to the animal beside him he said, "This is our big chance for a double-quick beeline job, Daisy. Think you can do it?"

Daisy, the rock hog, barked and wagged her tail.

"Just a minute," said Febold. "What kind of tunnel is a double-quick beeline tunnel? I want nothing but the best."

"That's what you're getting," answered Big Steve. "Daisy will start from this end, I'll start from the Florida end, and we'll meet in the middle."

But Febold was shaking his head. "You'll never make it," he declared. "You'll never in the wide world meet in the middle!"

And all evening long, from time to time, he'd shake his head and say, "Never make it!" In the morning, walking across the prairie with Big Steve and Daisy, to the starting point of the Nebraska end of the tunnel, he was still saying it.

Now this was the best thing that could have happened. Daisy was so upset by Febold's doubts that she made up her mind to drive a perfect beeline tunnel. She would NOT get sidetracked chasing small animals.

At last the three arrived at the Nebraska starting point. Big Steve said, "Okay, Daisy, start tunneling in a straight line." Then he set her nose in the exact direction she was to tunnel. When he saw that she had a good start, he hurried down to Florida to begin his end of the tunnel.

As he worked, Big Steve began to wonder if Daisy really would bore in a straight line. He was just about to decide that she had failed him, when who should come bursting through but Daisy

herself. She was so happy to see him that she almost knocked him down. Big Steve shouted, "Daisy, you old rock hog, you did it! You did it!" And they set off through Daisy's part of the tunnel to Febold's place. The fine weather had already started moving up from Florida and the walk was very pleasant.

When they finally reached the Nebraska end of the tunnel, they found a big crowd waiting for them. And Febold Feboldson was right out in front to greet them. He slapped Big Steve on the back and

shouted, "I knew you could do it!" Then he stuck his face into the tunnel and sniffed loudly. "Mmmm!" he exclaimed. "Smell that delightful Florida weather!"

Febold had a big party for the crowd. A few people from the neighboring state of Kansas had heard of the plan and had come up for the event. They stood around enjoying the Florida sunshine that came pouring out of the tunnel. Finally they asked if they could have a little of it for their own state.

"Sure!" said Big Steve.

"No!" Febold shook his head. "Nebraska can use all the Florida weather it can get—and then some."

That winter turned out to be a record one for both Nebraska and Kansas, but for different reasons.

In Nebraska, from October on, the snow lay thirteen feet, five-and-a-half inches deep. Big Steve and Daisy, who were staying with Febold, had never seen such a winter. But even when the snow reached the tops of the windows, Febold thought nothing of it. "It's going to take a lot of that Florida weather to have an effect on this winter," he said.

One day Big Steve looked at the calendar and was startled to see that it was already the third

of March. He knew Febold had no idea it was so late. "I should dig through that snow and see how the bore is doing," Big Steve said. "It may be clogged up."

"Good idea," Febold answered gloomily. "The stove's not drawing too well—snow must be over the chimney by now."

So, leaving Daisy behind since she wasn't very good on soft stuff, the tunnelman opened the door and started burrowing through the solid wall of snow. First he burrowed upward to unplug the chimney. He stuck his head out for a moment and looked around. There was nothing but snow everywhere. Then he burrowed under again, toward the weather tunnel.

When he got there he found that the mouth was indeed clogged up. He began tunneling, thinking that the snow at the mouth was what was holding back the weather. But even when he had at last holed through the snow that had drifted into the tunnel, there was still no sign of Florida weather behind it. He walked underground clear across Nebraska into Kansas. That's where he found the trouble.

The Kansans, without so much as a by-your-leave, had opened up a hole in the tunnel. All that good Florida weather was pouring out into Kansas!

That was the year that Kansans remember as the "Year-without-a-Winter." The thermometer stayed around eighty degrees every day and a fine salt breeze swept continually over the state. They grew two extra crops of corn that winter.

Big Steve plugged up the hole and hurried back to tell Febold. Febold was beside himself with rage. He'd show those Kansans! When he finally calmed down a bit, he sent two Indians to patrol the tunnel so the Kansans would leave it alone.

The fine Florida weather began coming through at last. The snow thawed rapidly, and people were beginning to say that Nebraska had the best weather in the world.

One day, shortly after this, Febold was fishing on the riverbank when the two Indians he had posted in the tunnel came whirling out on a terrific blast of wind. They just had time to yell, "Hurricane!" as they shot past him.

In all his glowing praises of Florida weather, Febold had never once thought of hurricanes. Well, while the people in Florida were getting ready for that hurricane, the Nebraskans were having it. Rain came down in such buckets that it almost floated Nebraska into neighboring Iowa. The hundred-mile wind tore the state line to pieces. For a while nobody could tell what was Nebraska and what was someplace else.

After three days the storm died down. As soon as it was over, some of Febold's friends came to see him. They thanked him for all he had done for Nebraska in the past, and would now thank him to stop importing other people's weather into the state.

When they left, some people from Florida came in. They said, "This past winter we had hardly any weather at all because you were piping it out of the state. We're telling you here and now that Florida weather is not for export—except, of course, the hurricanes. If you want some of our weather, come down and use it on the premises."

"I'll plug up the tunnel," said Big Steve.

"Okay," sighed Febold.

So Big Steve plugged up both ends. Then, feeling sorry for his friend, he tried to cheer him up. But

Febold only shook his head. "It's all right. Steve. It wasn't your fault. But there's nothing more I can do here so I'm off to California—no hurricanes there, just a little earthquake now and then."

As for Big Steve, he drove many a famous tunnel after that. But the one he is proudest of is the double-quick beeline weather bore. And even though it was plugged up after that first winter, he never tires of telling about it wherever tunnel-men get together.

"Why, Daisy and I joined the two parts of that bore smooth as silk and not a turn in the whole 1,453 miles of it!" he declares.

And Daisy sits at his feet, trying to look modest about her part in that famous job.

In the fourteenth century a famous English author wrote about a "day's eye." If the bright yellow center of the **daisy** reminded him of the sun, how would the petals add to that image?

Using Context Clues

As you know, there are several kinds of context clues that you can use to discover the meaning of words. Read the following fable. Then, in your own words, tell the meaning of each underlined word and explain which context clues helped you.

It had been a hot, dry summer. Only *one* small mountain spring bubbled with water! A goat and a lion came at the same time to this spring. Both animals were planning to quench their thirst.

At once they began arguing, quarreling about which of them should drink first. They were so intent that they even forgot their thirst! As they were about to attack each other, something made them look up. Many vultures were hovering, patiently circling overhead. When the winner left, the birds would pounce on the vanquished.

With silly smiles the lion and the goat said in chorus, "Dear friend, it is my pleasure to offer YOU the first drink!"

Moral: It is better to capitulate than to chance becoming food for vultures.

Check your word meanings in the Glossary.

THE BEWILDERING BUTTERCUPS

Scientists know that weather conditions on the earth have not always been the same. There have been very warm periods, very cold periods, wet periods, dry periods, and some in between. Though these changes usually take a long time to come about, this has not ALWAYS been true.

In the year 1900, while hunting in northern Asia, a Russian stumbled over the body of a huge animal. The creature was frozen in the ice with only its head sticking out. The animal was far too big for the man to dig out or move himself. Instead, he axed off the tusks and took them to the nearest trading post to sell.

The manager there bought the tusks and then asked about the rest of the beast. From what the hunter told him, the man recognized it as a mammoth, a kind of elephant that had died out about 10,000 years ago. According to Russian law, all mammoth and other frozen animal discoveries were to be reported to the government. The hunter did this, and a group of scientists was sent to the spot.

The men put up a wooden building around the body. Then they lighted fires to thaw out the beast. Finally they packed up the parts, refroze them in the cold air, and shipped them by sled to the railroad station. Later the animal would be mounted in a Russian museum. Though mammoths had been found before, this was a most unusual discovery. The scientists knew that they had a real mystery on their hands.

When this mammoth was found, it was sitting on its back legs. One of its front legs was raised. Except for parts of the head, which had been eaten by wolves, the animal was perfectly preserved. It was so fresh that the meat could even be eaten —if anyone cared to eat "elephant" meat. Most amazing of all, there were buttercups on its tongue!

These clues led the scientists to believe that when the animal lived, this part of northern Asia had been warm. Today it is a land of everlasting ice and snow. In fact the coldest temperatures in the world have been recorded near this area!

Just before the mammoth died it had been feeding on grass and flowers in the warm sunshine. Then, in a matter of seconds, the temperature dropped. Suddenly the animal was frozen. It happened so fast that the mammoth had not had a chance to swallow its meal! Not one part of the animal even began to decay! From that time on northern Asia has been a frozen land.

It has been suggested that to quick-freeze a mammoth, the temperature would have to drop almost at once to more than one hundred fifty degrees below zero. What force could have caused such a sudden and complete change in the weather? Could such a thing ever happen again in some part of the world? Scientists have many ideas about it, but they cannot be sure of any of them. It remains an unsolved mystery.

Many languages have had a word similar to our word **clue**, but meaning "a ball" or "a ball of thread." In a Greek myth a ball of thread was used to find a way out of a maze. Today a clue may help us "thread" our way to the solution of a problem.

THE HAPPY RAIN

This is a radio play based on a story of the same name. It may be read silently or performed as a make-believe radio show.

CHARACTERS		*SOUNDS*
ANNOUNCER	VOICE 4	DOOR SLAMMING
MOTHER	THIN MAN	KNOCKING ON DOOR
RAYMOND	WISE MAN	CREAKING DOOR
YOLANDE	BEARDED MAN	DOOR CLOSING
FAT MAN	SCIENTIST	MOTOR RUNNING
VOICE 1	PHILOSOPHER	
VOICE 2	MAYOR	
VOICE 3	LADY	

ANNOUNCER. Let's Soar to Adventure!

MUSIC—THEME, UP AND UNDER

ANNOUNCER. As a public service, radio station WISH presents a play written especially for children. Our story is called "The Happy Rain."

MUSIC—THEME, UP AND OUT

ANNOUNCER. The people of Troekan were very fortunate. No other village could boast of such fine, glorious rain. Rain that flooded gardens with dazzling flowers. Rain that made music as it pattered on tile roofs. Rain that drenched their clothes and muddied their streets. It was a joy to live in Troekan. Now, as this story begins, it was a typical day in Troekan—a real soaker. School, which for reasons of health was held outdoors in the rain, had just been dismissed. In one of the houses, a mother's voice said,

MOTHER. What—Raymond and Yolande—still in the house on such a fine rainy day? Quick—out into the streets—or do I have to toss you both out of the window?

RAYMOND. (*Laughing*) Oh, Mother, you're always joking.

YOLANDE. Of course, we're going right now.

MOTHER. (*Calling after them*) And, mind—you come back soaked to the skin—else I'll lock you both out.

SOUND—DOOR SLAMMING

YOLANDE. Mother knows we'll get soaked to the skin, and muddy, and dirty, too. Don't we every day?

RAYMOND. Of course we do. What shall we play today—mud-rolling, puddle-jumping, or hide-and-splash?

YOLANDE. We can dig a tremendous tunnel right under the street and make believe we are rabbits.

RAYMOND. Yes, and we can scare everybody that comes by.

YOLANDE. Let's go!

MUSIC—BRIDGE

ANNOUNCER. That night a howling storm came up. Starting with terrible suddenness, it mounted to a great fury. The villagers shook in their beds. When morning finally came, the tempest ended and a silence even more terrible than the storm settled over the village. In their room, Yolande whispered to her brother,

YOLANDE. How very funny. You can't hear anything when it's so quiet. Not even the rain pattering on the roof.

RAYMOND. I think I'm afraid, Yolande.

YOLANDE. I'd be afraid, too, if I knew what there was to be afraid about. Go to the window, Raymond, and see what has happened.

RAYMOND. You go.

YOLANDE. Oh, Raymond. Boys are much braver than girls. Please go to the window.

RAYMOND. I don't feel very brave.

YOLANDE. Now, Raymond.

RAYMOND. Oh, all right—(*Fade off*)—if I have to.

YOLANDE. Well? Is there anything to be afraid about?

RAYMOND. (*Off mike*) I—I think so.

YOLANDE. What is it?

RAYMOND. (*Off mike*) I think—I think it is the end of the world. It's stopped raining!

MUSIC—BRIDGE

ANNOUNCER. Can you imagine how it would be if the sun suddenly disappeared? Or if the moon disappeared? Or the stars? Or the sky? Well, so it was with the people of Troekan and their rain. There had never been a time in their entire history when it had ever stopped before. But now it had. Something would have to be done. Very carefully, notes were passed from house to house. At last it was decided to meet in the village square and make plans. Then one of the villagers, who was very fat, stepped forward and said,

FAT MAN. People of Troekan. Something, yes indeed, something must be done. What good, now really, what good does it do us to sit in our homes and shake with fear? No good at all. No good at all. It has stopped, yes, it has definitely stopped raining in Troekan. Well, let us make it start again.

CROWD. (*All agreeing*) Yes! Good idea! Hear! Hear!

VOICE 1. But how are we to do it?

VOICE 2. What is to be done?

VOICE 3. How are we to go about it?

VOICE 4. What should we do?

FAT MAN. Ah—that is, yes, that certainly is, indeed, a question. Thin man, have you an idea?

THIN MAN. I just thought of something. I believe it is a good idea—and here it is. In our sad village live three men—and one is a very wise old man —and one is a great scientist—and the other is an eminent philosopher—and surely one of them must know how to make the rain fall—and why not ask them?

CROWD. Yes, yes! Of course! A good idea!

VOICE 1. Whom shall we ask first?

VOICE 2. The wise old man.

VOICE 3. Yes, he's one hundred and seventy years old. Surely he has lived long enough to know how to make rain fall.

VOICE 4. Who will go to ask him?

RAYMOND. I'll go. The wise old man likes boys.

CROWD. Yes, Raymond will go! He'll find the answer! Three cheers for Raymond!

MUSIC—BRIDGE

ANNOUNCER. When Raymond arrived at the old man's house, he found him standing on his head.

RAYMOND. Wise old man, why are you standing on your head?

WISE MAN. I have been standing on my feet for one hundred and seventy years—and they were beginning to grow tired. Now I'm standing on my head, so as to give my feet a rest.

RAYMOND. What a wonderful idea! I'd love to stand on my head.

WISE MAN. My feet hardly hurt at all now.

RAYMOND. Really?

WISE MAN. My head aches somewhat, though.

RAYMOND. I see. But the reason I came was to ask you how we can make it rain again.

WISE MAN. Everyone should stand on his head.

RAYMOND. What? . . . Will that make it rain? If we all stood on our heads would the rain start falling?

WISE MAN. Probably have to wear a hat, though.

RAYMOND. Oh, how really wise you are!

WISE MAN. (*Grumbling*) Yes, yes, probably need a hat.

RAYMOND. Thank you, sir. I'll tell the people.

MUSIC—BRIDGE

ANNOUNCER. When Raymond told the villagers all that had happened, they wondered what it could mean. Was the old man talking about his aching feet—or was he telling them how to make it rain? Nevertheless, the people of Troekan stood on their heads. They did everything standing on their heads. They went for walks, they carried their umbrellas, they ate their suppers—standing on their heads. For three days they balanced themselves on their heads, and still no rain. So it was decided to send a bearded man to see the scientist, for the scientist liked men with beards. But when the bearded man arrived, he found the scientist's home boarded up.

BEARDED MAN. Scientist, are you in there?

SOUND—KNOCKING ON DOOR

BEARDED MAN. Hello, there, are you at home?

SOUND—CREAKING DOOR

SCIENTIST. Go away, go away. Don't come any closer to my house. It is full of secret and scientific inventions. You must not see them. They are secret. Secret. Secret. Go away.

BEARDED MAN. But, sir, it has stopped raining in Troekan. We want to know how to make it start again.

SCIENTIST. Hah! A simple matter. But remember —don't come any closer to my house. Full of secrets, you know. Wait—I shall come out.

SOUND—DOOR CLOSING

SCIENTIST. I must ask my secret machine. Just a minute.

SOUND—MOTOR RUNNING, UP AND OUT

SCIENTIST. Well, old sir, I have solved the problem. But first—must you stand on your head, so? It makes me quite dizzy.

BEARDED MAN. The wise old man said that if we would stand on our heads, it would rain.

SCIENTIST. (*Laughing*) Such nonsense. Why, my machine told me why there was no rain. You see, rain comes from clouds. Now, the holes in the clouds that the rain comes through have gotten all clogged up. You must make new holes in the clouds, and let the rain out. Simple, eh? Hah, we scientists are all very simple—secret and simple.

BEARDED MAN. How marvelous! Why didn't we think of that? But-but-but how are we to make new holes in the clouds?

SCIENTIST. Why, just get some cannons and shoot new holes in the clouds. Simple—simple—simple—

MUSIC—BRIDGE

ANNOUNCER. The villagers were overjoyed at the news. Quickly they sprang to their feet again and got together all the cannons they could find. Before long they were blazing away at the clouds. The shooting went on for three days, but still no rain. The people met in the village square again—all hoarse, a little deaf, and very unhappy. This time they agreed it would be best to go to the philosopher. And this time, they sent Yolande. The philosopher lived in the forest—on a bearskin. That was his only home. Books, thousands of

them, were scattered all over. He was reading when Yolande timidly approached.

YOLANDE. Oh—oh—Mister Philosopher—please—Sir Philosopher. It has stopped raining in Troekan. Can you please tell us how to turn it on again?

PHILOSOPHER. Rain—is it? I think I can coax the rain to fall. Ah, here it is—in this book—right on this page. Is it not wonderful how we can find the answers to all our problems in ancient books? Our ancient teachers knew the answers to everything. And today we can do nothing but follow their teachings—and wonder at their wonderfulness.

YOLANDE. Oh, sir, you're so awfully smart!

PHILOSOPHER. Yes. Our ancient teachers—how wise they were. Now, to make it rain—one must put a paper bag over one's head.

YOLANDE. A paper bag?

PHILOSOPHER. Why, of course—a paper bag. It says so—right here. This book was written by an ancient teacher. And to this day no one has dared to doubt a word he said. Why, here on these pages he lists all the things that a paper bag will cure. From head colds to sprained ankles. Truly remarkable.

YOLANDE. Yes, sir. Thank you, sir.

MUSIC—BRIDGE

ANNOUNCER. Yolande raced back to the village square. The people were amazed when they realized it took only a paper bag to make it rain. Before long, everyone was wearing the strange headdress. For three days this went on and the people of Troekan became rather tired of it all. Yet, for all their trouble, there was not so much as a drizzle. Back to the village square they went, and at last it was decided to send a lady to ask the mayor what should be done. The mayor lived in a huge house. The lady had to search through all the rooms until she found him.

MAYOR. Leave me alone. Can't you see that I'm busy? So busy. Busy. Busy. Go away. I am so busy.

LADY. But, Mr. Mayor—

MAYOR. Ah—dear lady. What can I do for you?

LADY. Oh, mayor, it has stopped raining in Troekan. We have gone to the wise old man and he told us to stand on our heads. But there was no rain. Then we went to the scientist and he told us to shoot cannon balls at the clouds. But that did not help either. The philosopher told us to cover our heads with paper bags. Still there was no rain. What are we to do?

MAYOR. No rain in Troekan, eh? I hadn't noticed. I have been so busy you know. No rain, well, well. Ah—I have it, dear lady. I think the fault must lie with you people of Troekan. For if the three wise men are right, then somebody else must be wrong. Do you follow me?

LADY. I think so.

MAYOR. Well, then, I believe you must do what the three wise men told you to do—all at once. Yes, you must stand on your heads, shoot cannon balls at the clouds, and wear those paper bags. Then you will have rain. No doubt about it. I am right.

LADY. Oh, thank you, dear mayor.

MUSIC—BRIDGE

ANNOUNCER. If a traveler had happened upon Troekan that day, he would have thought they

had all gone mad. He would have seen the people standing on heads that were hidden by paper bags, shooting cannon balls at the sky. But after three days, the people of Troekan lost all hope. It did not rain. They gave up and went back to their homes. There was nothing else to do. In their room, Raymond asked his sister,

RAYMOND. What are we to do now?

YOLANDE. Spend the rest of our lives in bed.

RAYMOND. But, Yolande, I wouldn't want to do that.

YOLANDE. There is nothing else to do when it is the end of the world.

RAYMOND. We used to have so much fun. Let's pretend it is raining.

YOLANDE. I don't want to pretend. I want it really to rain.

RAYMOND. Oh, so do I.

YOLANDE. I know! We must tell the clouds we want rain. How can the clouds know we want rain if we never, ever told them so? Of course, we stood on our heads. Now, we knew that was supposed to bring rain—but did the clouds know? And when we shot cannon balls at them, what could they think but that we were trying to drive them away forever? And even though the paper bags must surely cure head colds and sprained ankles —still, the clouds might have thought we didn't even want to look at them. We never told them we wanted rain. Oh, Raymond, we must tell them. But how—how?

RAYMOND. Maybe, if I got my balloon I—

YOLANDE. Balloon? Raymond, that is just the thing. I can write the message and put it in a bottle, and then we can tie it to the balloon, and away it will fly to the clouds. Oh, Raymond, how clever you are!

MUSIC—BRIDGE

ANNOUNCER. In a short time the excited cries of Raymond and Yolande brought the villagers running from every direction.

VOICE 1. What is it? What new misfortune has happened now?

YOLANDE. No misfortune at all. My brother and I have sent a message to the clouds.

VOICE 2. What on earth for?

RAYMOND. Yolande thought the clouds should be told we want rain.

VOICE 3. Why, they're wiser than the wise men of Troekan!

VOICE 4. But—what was the message you sent?

YOLANDE. I wrote: REALLY—REALLY—WE DO LOVE YOU.

MUSIC—BRIDGE

ANNOUNCER. There was very little sleep that night. A mysterious wind came up to rouse the villagers. And when morning came, the people of Troekan heard another sound—a strange sound. Like a tap-tap-tapping. It was the rain falling on the tile roofs! It was the end of the end of the world! Excitedly everyone gathered in the village square.

CROWD. Hurray for Raymond and Yolande!

VOICE 1. Yes, but did they really accomplish the miracle? Could it have been their message?

VOICE 2. Of course not, the balloon had nothing to do with it. Probably would have rained anyway.

VOICE 3. But we tried so many ways to make rain fall. And they all ended in failure. While now, just as the balloon disappeared, the rain returned.

VOICE 4. We should build a statue of Raymond and Yolande and their precious balloon. We should place it in the village square. For they are the greatest heroes Troekan has ever had.

CROWD. Hear! Hear! Good idea! Yes, a statue!

MUSIC—BRIDGE

ANNOUNCER. The people had a glorious celebration that day—as the cooling Troekan rain drenched their clothes, muddied their streets, and watered the young seedlings of the soon-to-be-growing plants. And, because it rained happily ever after, the people of Troekan lived happily ever after.

MUSIC—THEME, UP AND UNDER

ANNOUNCER. You have been listening to "The Happy Rain," an adventure written especially for children and produced by station WISH.

MUSIC—THEME, UP AND OUT

GLOSSARY

Pronunciation Key

The pronunciation key will help you to understand what the diacritical marks mean in the Glossary of *Trade Winds*, Basic Fourth Reader, *Strand 1*.

The principal, or heavy, accent is indicated by the mark ′ after a syllable. In some words another syllable is also accented, but not so heavily. Such a syllable has the mark ′ after it—called a secondary accent.

Many foreign languages are spoken with some sounds which do not occur in English. A symbol for such a sound is given at the end of this pronunciation key.

a as in hat	o as in hot	th as in thin
ā as in āge	ō as in ōpen	ᴛʜ as in then
ã as in cãre	ô as in ôrder	
ä as in fäther		zh as in measure
	oi as in oil	
e as in let	ou as in house	ə represents:
ē as in ēqual		a in about
ėr as in tėrm	u as in cup	e in taken
	ů as in fůll	i in pencil
i as in it	ü as in rüle	o in lemon
ī as in īce	ū as in ūse	u in circus

French ɴ: Do not pronounce the ɴ. Its purpose is to show that the vowel before it is spoken with the nasal passage open so that the breath passes through both the nose and the mouth.

The pronunciation system and key employed in this publication is from the Thorndike-Barnhart Dictionary Program and is used by permission of Scott, Foresman and Company. © 1962.

A. General Glossary

a

-able (*suffix*), having; the quality of being. See **-ible**

ache (āk), a steady, dull pain

a dapt (ə dapt'), to make fit; to adjust

adjust (ə just'), to get used to; to set right

aer o naut (ãr'ə nôt), an airship or balloon pilot; anyone who travels in an airship or a balloon

-al (*suffix*), like; pertaining to

a larm (ə lärm'), fear; a device that makes noise to wake people

A las ka (ə las'kə), a state in the United States

al ly (al' i), a helper; a person or nation joined with another for a special purpose

A.M., the hours from midnight to noon

a maze (ə māz'), to surprise greatly

-an (*suffix*), of; having to do with

-ance (*suffix*), the act of; the fact of

an chor (ang' kər), a heavy object used to hold a ship in place

an cient (ān'shənt), very old; of times long past

-ant (*suffix*), one that

an to nym (an'tə nim), a word that means the opposite of another word

ap pen dix (ə pen'diks), a small growth attached to the large intestine

Ap pi an Way (ap'i ən), a famous Roman road

ar e a (ãr'i ə), place; region

ar gue (är'gū), to quarrel; to disagree

ar mor (är'mər), a covering worn to protect the body

-ary (*suffix*), a person or thing that has, goes, does, etc.

A sia (a'zhə), a continent

as par a gus (əs par'ə gəs), a plant, the shoots of which are used as a vegetable

as ter isk (as'tər isk), a star-shaped mark used to call attention to a footnote

as tro naut (as'trə nôt), the pilot or crew member of a space ship; one who sails among the stars

-ate (*suffix*), having

-ation (*suffix*), the act of being; the state of being

At lan tic (at lan'tik), an ocean east of North and South America

at tack (ə tak'), to fight against

au to mat ic (ô'tə mat'ik), having to do with moving by itself

awl (ôl), a pointed tool for making holes in wood or leather

b

bal ance (bal'əns), to keep steady; to be equal in weight; a pleasing arrangement of design

B.C., the initials which stand for the words "Before Christ"; used to designate the number of years *before* the birth of Christ in indicating dates

beam (bēm), the main support of a building or ship; a bright look or smile

bee line (bē′lĭn′), straight; the straightest way between two places

ben e fit (ben′ə fit), to give help to

be stir (bi stėr′), to rouse to action; to stir up

be wil der (bi wil′dər), to puzzle; to confuse

blun der (blun′dər), a mistake; to stumble

bob (bob), to move up and down with short quick motions

bore (bôr), to make a passage by digging out; the passage made by digging

Bos ton (bôs′tən), a city in the state of Massachusetts

brass (bras), a yellow metal

breed (brēd), a kind or a certain type of animal

bur den (bėr′dən), a load; something or someone to care for

burst (bėrst), to break open; to break out

bur y (ber′i), to cover up; to put in the earth; to hide

c

Cal i for nia (kal′ə fôrn′yə), a state in the United States

Can a da (kan′ə də), a country north of the United States

can ni bal (kan′ə bəl), a person who eats human flesh

ca pit u late (kə pich′ù lāt), to come to terms; to give in

cap ture (kap′chər), to take by force; to make a prisoner of

cas u al (kazh′ü əl), not planned

cas u al ty (kazh′ü əl ti), an accident; a mishap

cel lar (sel′ər), an underground room

cem e ter y (sem′ə ter′i), a graveyard; a place for burying the dead

cent (sent), a coin, one hundred of which make a dollar

chem i cal (kem′ə kəl), any substance that is used in chemistry

chem is try (kem′is tri), the study of substances to discover what they are made of, under what conditions the substances change, and how one substance affects another

Chi na (chi′nə), a country in Asia

cho rus (kô′rəs), a group who speak the same words at the same time; to say together

Cin cin nat i (sin′sə nat′i), a city in the state of Ohio

civ il (siv′əl), not wild or savage; cultured

cleave (klēv), to cut; to split

clog (klog), to stop up

---

hat, āge, cãre, fäther; let, ēqual, tėrm; it, ĭce; hot, ōpen, ôrder; oil; house; cup, fùll, rüle, ūse; th, thin; ᴛʜ, then; zh, measure; ə represents *a* in about, *e* in taken, *i* in pencil, *o* in lemon, *u* in circus

coax (kōks), to talk into doing something by using kind words; to persuade

col lect (kə lekt′), to gather together

col o ny (kol′ə ni), a settlement

com- (*prefix*), with; together

com plain (kəm plān′), to say something is wrong

com pli cat ed (kom′plə kāt′id), made up of many parts; intricate

con- (*prefix*), a form of **com-**

con ceive (kən sēv′), to imagine; to think up

Con es to ga wagon (kon′is tō′gə), a large covered wagon

con tent (kon′tent), all things inside

con tent (kən tent′), satisfied; pleased

con tin ue (kən tin′ū), to go on with

con trib ute (kən trib′ūt), to give help; to add to

cour age (kėr′ij), bravery

cre vasse (krə vas′), a deep crack in ice, as in a glacier

crew (krü), a group of people working together

cru el (krü′əl), mean; wicked; savage

cu ri ous (kūr′i əs), eager to know; strange

cur rent (kėr′ənt), a stream of moving air

d

damp er (dam′pər), a movable plate to control the draft in a stove or furnace

dan gle (dang′gəl), to swing or hang loosely

de- (*prefix*), down

de cay (di kā′), to rot; to spoil

dec o rate (dek′ə rāt), to make beautiful

de gree (di grē′), a unit for measuring temperature

del i cate (del′ə kit), dainty; finely woven; thin

dense (dens), thick

de ter mine (di tėr′mən), to decide firmly

de vice (di vīs′), a plan; a machine; a mechanical invention for a certain purpose

di rect (də rekt′), to follow a course or path; to manage

dis- (*prefix*), not; loss; the opposite of

dis guise (dis gīz′), to dress to look like someone else; an outfit worn to hide one's real self

disk (disk), a round, thin, flat object

dis may (dis mā′), fearful surprise; fear of what is about to happen

dis tinct (dis tingkt′), clear; easily seen

dis turb (dis tėrb′), to bother; to break in upon with noise or change

dive-bomb (dīv′bom′), to plunge downward suddenly and swiftly

-dom (*suffix*), the condition of being

draft (draft), a device for regulating a current of air in a heating system

drench (drench), to soak

drought (drout), a long period of dry weather

439

---

drowse (drouz), to be half asleep

du ra ble (dür′ə bəl), lasting a long time; having hardness

e

el e gant (el′ə gənt), fine; lovely

em i nent (em′ə nənt), well known; outstanding

em pire (em′pir), a group of states or countries under the same ruler or government

en- (*prefix*), make; in; into

-en (*suffix*), made of; consisting of

-ence (*suffix*), the condition of being

en dur ance (en dür′əns), power to last; the quality of being hard

Eng land (ing′glənd), a part of the island of Great Britain, in Europe

-ent (*suffix*), one that

-er (*suffix*), a person or thing that; one who is in. See **-or**

-ern (*suffix*), of; toward

es ca la tor (es′kə lā′tər), a moving stairway

-eth (*suffix*), a form of **-th**

Eu rope (ūr′əp), a continent

Eu ro pe an (ūr′ə pē′ən), having to do with the continent of Europe, or its people

e vent (i vent′), a happening

ex- (*prefix*), out; from

ex am ine (eg zam′ən), to look at closely and carefully

ex ert (eg zėrt′), to make an effort; to try hard

ex pert (eks′pėrt), a person who knows a great deal about some special thing

ex plode (eks plōd′), to blow up noisily

ex tend (eks tend′), to stretch out; to continue in a direction

f

fa ble (fā′bəl), an imaginary story which teaches a lesson

fab u lous (fab′ū ləs), amazing; imaginary

fade (fād), to lose color; to disappear

faint (fānt), to lose awareness; weak or dim

fa mil iar (fə mil′yər), well known; common

fash ion (fash′ən), style

fierce (fērs), wild or savage; strong or intense

fier y (fir′i), flaming; burning

flight (flīt), a set of stairs; a trip through the air

Flor i da (flôr′ə də), a state in the United States

fo cus (fō′kəs), to bring clearly into view; to call attention to; to adjust a lens to make a clear image

fore- (*prefix*), before; in front of

fore cast (fôr′kast′), to say beforehand; to predict

---

hat, āge, cãre, fäther; let, ēqual, tėrm; it, īce; hot, ōpen, ôrder; oil; house; cup, fùll, rüle, ūse; th, thin; ᴛʜ, then; zh, measure; ə represents *a* in about, *e* in taken, *i* in pencil, *o* in lemon, *u* in circus

frame (frām), a support; one picture on a strip of movie film

France (frans), a country in Europe

fringe (frinj), a trimming made of threads and cords; the edge

-ful (*suffix*), full of; having

fu ry (fū′ri), fierceness; wildness

g

gain (gān), to reach

gan der (gan′dər), a male goose

Gaul (gôl), an ancient country in Europe

gem (jem), a beautiful stone; a jewel

GEM (jem), a coined word for a type of vehicle, formed by using the first letters of the words "Ground Effects Machine"

gist (jist), the main idea

gla cier (glā′shər), a big mass of ice that moves slowly down a mountain or along a valley

glis ten (glis′ən), to shine; to sparkle

gorge (gôrj), a deep narrow valley, usually steep and rocky

gos ling (goz′ling), a young goose

-graph (*word element*), to write

grate ful (grāt′fəl), thankful; full of gratitude

gray (grā), a color made by mixing white and black

Greek (grēk), having to do with the country of Greece, its people, or their language

grey (grā), gray

grind (grīnd), to make something work by turning a crank; a harsh sound

ground (ground), to keep from taking off

guest (gest), a visitor; a caller

gulch (gulch), a deep, narrow ravine with steep sides

Gulf of Ri ga (rē′gə), a large bay of the Baltic Sea in Europe

h

har vest (här′vist), a gathering in of crops

haze (hāz), a dreamlike state; an unclearness of the mind; a fog

Hen der son (hen′dər sən), a city in the state of New York

he ro (hē′rō), one who is admired for his actions

hes i tate (hez′ə tāt), to hold back; to pause

-hood (*suffix*), a group of

hos tage (hos′tij), a person held by an enemy until an agreement is carried out

host ess (hōs′tis), a woman who receives guests

hov er (huv′ər), to circle overhead; to stay in one place over something

hur ri cane (hėr′ə kān), a storm with strong wind and, often, very heavy rain

i

-ian (*suffix*), a form of **-an**

-ible (*suffix*), having. See **-able**

-ic (*suffix*), having to do with

im- (*prefix*), a form of **in-**, used before *b*, *m*, *p*

in- (*prefix*), not; the opposite of

In dia (in′diə), a region in Asia

in spect (in spekt′), to look at carefully

in tent (in tent′), paying close attention to something

inter- (*prefix*), between

in ter rupt (in′tə rupt′), to break in upon

-ion (*suffix*), the act of; the state of

I o wa (i′ə wə), a state in the United States

Ire land (ir′lənd), one of the British Isles

-ish (*suffix*), belonging to

-ism (*suffix*), the act of being

-ist (*suffix*), one who knows about

-ity (*suffix*), the state or condition of being

-ive (*suffix*), having to do with; likely to

-ize (*suffix*), make; become

k

Kan sas (kan′zəs), a state in the United States

l

Lan cas ter (lang′kəs tər), a city in the state of Pennsylvania

launch (lônch), to start

league (lēg), a group of people joined together for a purpose, such as playing ball

leg end (lej′ənd), a story coming from the past, which may or may not be based on fact

-less (*suffix*), without; that does not; that cannot be

Let tish (let′ish), having to do with the country of Latvia in Europe, its people, or their language

lev el (lev′əl), height; even

lim er ick (lim′ər ik), a funny verse having five lines

liq uo rice (lik′ə ris), a plant, the root of which gives a substance used as a flavoring

lit er al (lit′ər əl), actual; for a fact

loup-ga rou (lü′gə rü′), a were-wolf; in folklore, a person who can change into a wolf but keep human intelligence

-ly (*suffix*), the manner of being; like

lye (li), a strong solution used in making soap

m

mad am (mad′əm), a polite title used in speaking to a lady

mad ame (mä däm′), madam

mag net (mag′nit), a piece of iron or steel that attracts another piece of iron or steel

Mal e ku la (mal′ə kü′lə), an island in the Pacific Ocean near Australia

man u fac ture (man′ū fak′chər), to make by hand or machine

mare (mãr), a female horse

Mars (märz), the fourth planet from the sun

---

hat, āge, cãre, fäther; let, ēqual, tėrm; it, ice; hot, ōpen, ôrder; oil; house; cup, full, rüle, ūse; th, thin; ŦH, then; zh, measure; ə represents *a* in about, *e* in taken, *i* in pencil, *o* in lemon, *u* in circus

mast (mast), a long pole set upright on a ship to support the sails and rigging

-ment (*suffix*), the act of; the state of

me ringue (mə rang'), a mixture of egg whites and sugar, beaten stiff

me sa (mā'sə), a flat-topped hill with steeply sloping sides

Me te or o log i ca (mē'ti ər ə-loj'i kə), a book by Aristotle

-meter (*word element*), a device for measuring

Mex i can (mek'sə kən), a person from the country of Mexico

Mich i gan (mish'ə gən), a state in the United States

Min ne so ta (min'ə sō'tə), a state in the United States

mir a cle (mir'ə kəl), a wonderful happening beyond the known laws of nature

mis- (*prefix*), bad

mis er y (miz'ər i), great unhappiness

mod ern (mod'ərn), present-day

mod est (mod'ist), shy; without wrongful pride

mous tache (mus'tash), mustache

mu se um (mū zē'əm), a place where interesting objects are displayed

mus tache (mus'tash), hair that grows on a man's upper lip

myth (mith), a story connected with the religion of an early civilization, told to explain something in nature

n

Ne bras ka (nə bras'kə), a state in the United States

ne ces si ty (nə ses'ə ti), great need; that which cannot be done without

nerve (nėrv), courage; bravery

-ness (*suffix*), the state or condition of being

New York (nü yôrk'), a city in the state of New York

o

Oak ley (ōk'li), a neighborhood in Cincinnati, Ohio

ob serve (əb zėrv'), to look at carefully; to notice

-or (*suffix*), a person or thing that. See **-er**

-ous (*suffix*), having; full of

p

pace (pās), to go as fast as; rate; speed

par tic u lar (pər tik'ū lər), special; especial

pa trol (pə trōl'), to guard; to watch

Penn syl va ni a (pen'səl vā'ni ə), a state in the United States

per form (pər fôrm'), to do something; to act

pe ri od (pēr' i əd), a space of time

Phil a del phi a (fil'ə del'fi ə), a city in the state of Pennsylvania

phi los o pher (fə los'ə fər), one who tries to understand and explain the truth underlying all knowledge

Phoe ni cian (fə nish'ən), having to do with the ancient country of Phoenicia, its people, or their language

pil lar (pil'ər), a post; a column

pin to (pin'tō), having spots of two colors

pitch (pich), to throw; a black, sticky substance made from tar

plan et (plan'it), a certain kind of heavenly body that moves around the sun

Pom peii (pom pā'), a city in ancient Italy

prai rie (prār'i), flat or rolling grassy land without trees

pram (pram), a type of flat-bottomed boat

pre his to ry (prē his'tə ri), before recorded history

prem is es (prem'is əz), grounds; property

pre serve (pri zėrv'), a place where wild animals are protected; to save

prick le (prik'əl), a small sharp point; a smarting feeling as from many sharp points

prin ci pal (prin'sə pəl), one who heads a school

pro ject (prə jekt'), to throw forward on a surface

P.T.A., the initials which stand for an organization, formed from the first letters of the words Parent-Teacher Association

Puer to Ri co (pwer'tō rē'kō), an island in the Atlantic Ocean, near the United States

pum ice (pum'is), a light, spongy stone thrown up from volcanoes

q

quench (kwench), to put a stop to

quilt (kwilt), a bed cover made of two pieces of cloth with padding in between, held together by stitching

r

ran dom (ran'dəm), without a plan or purpose

range (rānj), a place to practice shooting; a land for grazing; a line or row of mountains; to vary or change

ran som (ran'səm), a price demanded before a captive is freed

ra vine (rə vēn'), a long, deep narrow gorge worn by running water

re- (*prefix*), again; back

re cess (rē'ses), a time during which work stops

rec og nize (rek'əg nīz), to know again; to identify

ref er ee (ref'ər ē'), a judge of play in sports and games

res er va tion (rez'ər vā'shən), U.S. land set aside for a special purpose

riv et (riv'it), a metal bolt for holding steel beams together

Ro man (rō'mən), having to do with the city of Rome, or its people

---

hat, āge, cãre, fäther; let, ēqual, tėrm; it, ice; hot, ōpen, ôrder; oil; house; cup, fùll, rüle, ūse; th, thin; ᴛʜ, then; zh, measure; ə represents *a* in about, *e* in taken, *i* in pencil, *o* in lemon, *u* in circus

Rome (rōm), a city in the country of Italy

route (rüt), way to go; path

Rus sian (rush′ən), having to do with the country of Russia, its people, or their language

s

St. Louis (sānt lü′is), a city in the state of Missouri

San Juan (san hwän′), a city in Puerto Rico

Sap o Hill (sap′ō), a hill in ancient Rome

scud (skud), to move swiftly

seed (sēd), to drop chemicals from an airplane in an effort to produce rain; the thing from which a plant grows

ski (skē), to glide over the snow on metal or wooden boards of a special type

slug (slug), to hit hard

snooze (snüz), to sleep

snout (snout), the projecting part of an animal's head containing the nose, mouth, and jaws

soak (sōk), to make or become very wet

soar (sôr), to fly upward

so da (sō′də), a chemical used to manufacture soap; a soft drink

so lar (sō′lər), having to do with the sun

sol id (sol′id), not hollow; hard or firm; unbroken or continuous

so lo (sō′lō), something done by one person

So per ville (sō′pər vil), an imaginary Indian reservation

Spain (spān), a country in Europe

spang (spang), exactly

Span ish (span′ish), having to do with the country of Spain, its people, or their language

spec i men (spes′ə mən), one of a kind used to show what the others look like

spec ta cle (spek′tə kəl), a sight; a thing to look at

spec tac u lar (spek tak′ū lər), something very big and unusual to look at; showy

spec ta tor (spek′tā tər), an onlooker; one who looks on without taking part

spir it ed (spir′ə tid), lively

square (skwãr), firmly in the center; a figure with four equal sides; a space in a town, bounded by streets on four sides

square dance, a dance done by couples in a set form

stal lion (stal′yən), a full-grown male horse

-stat (*word element*), brought to a stand; fixed

stat ue (stach′ü), a likeness of a person or animal made of stone, wood, metal, etc.

stream (strēm), a steady flow

sty lus (stī′ləs), a pointed tool for writing on wax

sub stance (sub′stəns), material; what a thing is made of

sus pect (səs pekt′), to imagine to be so

swamp (swomp), wet, soft land

syl la ble (sil′ə bəl), part of a word pronounced as a unit

445

syn o nym (sin'ə nim), a word that means the same or nearly the same as another word

sys tem (sis'təm), a method; a group of people joined together for a purpose; a group of heavenly bodies

t

-teen (*word element*), ten

tele- (*word element*), far; over a distance

tem pest (tem'pist), a very bad storm with high winds

ter rif ic (tə rif'ik), very great; causing great fear

-th (*suffix*), tens; used to show tens

thatch (thach), straw, palm leaves, etc., used as a roof or covering

thermo- (*word element*), heat

ther mom e ter (thər mom'ə tər), an instrument for measuring temperature

ther mo stat (thėr'mə stat), an automatic device that keeps heat at a fixed or steady temperature

thread (thred), a thin cord used in sewing and weaving; to make one's way carefully through

thresh (thresh), to separate the seeds from the rest of the plant

thrust (thrust), to push with force

-tion (*suffix*), the act of; the state of

tomb stone (tüm'stōn'), a stone that marks the tomb or grave of a dead body

tore (tôr), ripped; moved quickly

trans- (*prefix*), across

trap (trap), a device to throw small objects into the air to be shot at

trea ty (trē'ti), an understanding, usually written, between nations

tres- (*prefix*), a form of **trans-**

tres pass (tres'pəs), to go on somebody's land without any right

trill (tril), a trembling sound

trim (trim), to arrange sails to fit wind and direction; to cut away parts

Troe kan (troi'kan'), an imaginary village

troop (trüp), a company, especially of soldiers

troupe (trüp), a company, especially a group of actors

twelve (twelv), two more than ten

twen ty (twen'ti), two times ten

twice (twis), two times; doubly

twin (twin), one of two persons or things very much alike

twist (twist), to wind; two or more strands wound together

-ty (*suffix*), tens; the state or condition of being. See **-ity**

---

hat, āge, cãre, fäther; let, ēqual, tėrm; it, ĭce; hot, ōpen, ôrder; oil; house; cup, fůll, rüle, ūse; th, thin; ᴛʜ, then; zh, measure; ə represents *a* in about, *e* in taken, *i* in pencil, *o* in lemon, *u* in circus

u

um pire (um′pir), a person who rules on the plays in a game between teams

un- (*prefix*), not; the opposite of

uni- (*word element*), one

U nit ed States (ū nit′id stāts′), a country in North America

-ure (*suffix*), the act of; the fact of

v

vague (vāg), not clear; not exact

val ley (val′i), a low land between hills and mountains

van quish (vang′kwish), to defeat; to beat

va por (vā′pər), moisture in the air that can be seen

ve hi cle (vē′ə kəl), a thing that carries people and goods

ven ture (ven′chər), a daring undertaking; to dare to say

Venus (vē′nəs), the second planet from the sun

voy age (voi′ij), a journey; a cruise

vul ture (vul′chər), a large bird that eats the flesh of dead animals

w

whirl (hwėrl), to spin; to rotate

wide-beamed (wïd′bēmd′), having broad supports as in a boat or ship

y

-y (*suffix*), resembling; full of; state

yes ter day (yes′tər di), the day before today

B. Characters

Al ex an der (al′ig zan′dər)
Al ice (al′is)
Al va ro (äl′vä rō)
A mel ia (ə mēl′yə)
An dro cles (an′drə klēz)
Ap pi us (ap′i əs)
A rach ne (ə rak′ni)
Ar is tot le (ar′is tot′əl)
A the na (ə thē′nə)
Be del ia (bi dēl′yə)
Black beard (blak′bērd′)
Braille (brāl)
But ler (but′lər)

Cae cus (sē′kəs)
Can di ta (kän dē′tə)
Char lotte (shär′lət)
Chou chou (shü′shü′)
Clau di us (klô′di əs)
Dai sy (dā′zi)
E dith (ē′dəth)
En dym i on (en dim′i ən)
Fe bold son (fi bōld′sən)
Ga ger (gā′jər)
Gal i le o (gal′ə lē′ō)
Georges (zhôrzh)
Gretch en (grech′ən)

447

Hank (hangk)
Han sen (han′sən)
Ha üy (a′ü ē′)
He phaes tion (hi fes′chən)
Ho mer (hō′mər)
How ard (hou′ərd)
Hug gins (hug′ənz)
Hyde (hid)
Jerry (jer′i)
John son (jon′sən)
Jo seph (jō′zəf)
Ka tie (kā′ti)
La Moun tane (lä mən tān′)
Le blanc (lə bläN′)
Lin da (lin′də)
Lord (lôrd)
Lou is (lü′i)
Lu cian (lü′shən)
Lur vy (lėr′vi)
Mar tin (mär′tən)
Mc Ad am (mək ad′əm)
Me loche (mə lôsh′)
Mi chel (mē′shel′)
Mo ses (mō′zis)
Muir (mūr)
Mu ñoz (mü nyôz′)
Na ga pa te (nä′gə pä′tā)

O dette (ô′det′)
Ol i ver (ol′ə vər)
O sa (ō′sə)
Pha e ton (fā′ə tən)
Pierre (pyãr)
Pol li wog (pol′i wog)
Pudge (puj)
Ra fa el (rä′fä əl)
Ray mond (rā′mənd)
Rog ers (roj′ərz)
Si las (sī′ləs)
Steve (stēv)
Stick een (stik ēn′)
Stubbs (stubz)
Sue (sü)
Tante (täNt)
Tem ple ton (tem′pəl tən)
Ter ry (ter′i)
Ti tus (tī′təs)
To by (tō′bi)
Tom a hawk (tom′ə hôk)
Treat (trēt)
Tucker (tuk′ər)
Ty ler (tī′lər)
Wil bur (wil′bər)
Yo lan de (yō lan′də)
Zuck er man (zuk′ər mən)

C. Radio Terms

bridge (brij), a music passage used to show a change of place or time

fade (fād), the actor moves toward, or backs away from, the microphone while speaking

off mike (ôf mīk), the actor stands at a distance from the microphone, or turns his head away from it, while speaking

theme (thēm), a melody used to set the mood for, or identify, a program

up and out (up′ənd out′), the music or sound gets louder, then softer, and stops

up and under (up′ənd un′dər), the music or sound gets louder, then softer, and continues under the scene

448